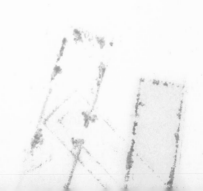

THE PEOPLES OF AFRICA

COLIN M. TURNBULL

THE PEOPLES
OF AFRICA

Illustrated by Richard M. Powers

THE WORLD PUBLISHING COMPANY

CLEVELAND AND NEW YORK

Published by The World Publishing Company
2231 West 110th Street, Cleveland 2, Ohio

Published simultaneously in Canada by
Nelson, Foster & Scott Ltd.

Library of Congress Catalog Card Number: 62–16364

CONTENTS

*Pronunciations for unfamiliar words
are given in the Index*

THE LAND OF AFRICA

Before we can even begin to understand Africa, its peoples, and their age-old traditions, we have to realize that this vast continent is not only one of the oldest in the world, but it is also one of the most varied. Its northern shore, along the Mediterranean, is for the most part lush and green, but not many miles inland runs the huge range of the Atlas Mountains, snow-capped and almost impassable in the winter. In winter, if you do manage to cross over, you come down on the other side directly into the dreadful heat of the Sahara Desert. This vast, arid region stretches right across the continent, three thousand miles from west to east and for a thousand miles south.

About halfway down the western "hump" the forest begins, and if you continued the line made by the lower edge of the hump—where the coast runs from west to east—you would come to the beginning of the dense tropical rain forest that covers the whole of central Africa. Between the forest and the desert there is woodland and savanna, lonely stretches of sparsely inhabited, thorny grassland, with only occasional sprinklings of acacia trees.

Over to the east, starting level with the northern edge of the

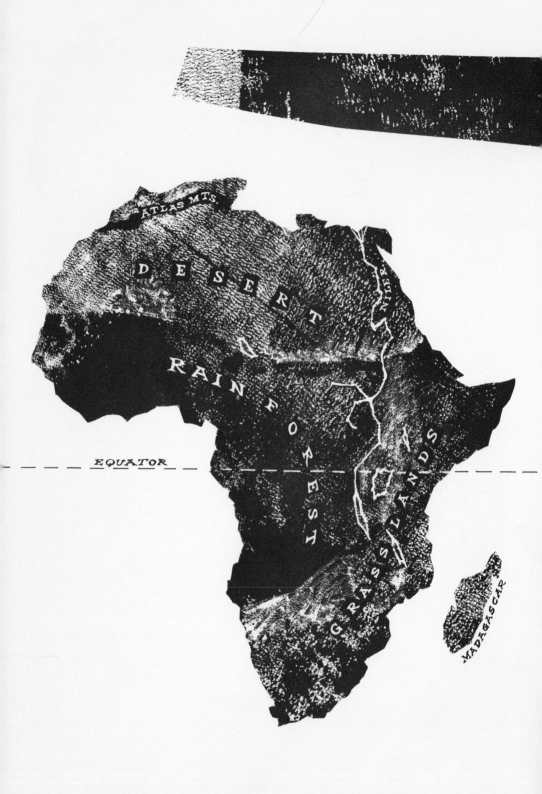

forest, lie the great lakes of Africa, a long chain of them, linked to the Nile and all but making an island of the whole of eastern Africa from Egypt right down to the Zambezi River, in Mozambique. West of the lakes is the rain forest, and to the east lie the African grasslands, rolling plains of green pasture land, studded with snow-capped mountains like the Ruwenzori (better known as the Mountains of the Moon), Mount Kenya, and Mount Kilimanjaro.

The plateau below these mountains is so high that even though it is right on the equator and is scorched by the sun during the daytime, it can be bitterly cold at night. The grasslands stretch on down the east coast into South Africa, where again you find mountains and plateaus and rolling hills, but where you also find the formidable Kalahari Desert.

9

Throughout the continent, from north to south, there is a maze of rivers, some of the longest in the world, and all their various tributaries and the adjoining streams. The Nile, the Niger, the Congo, and the Zambezi are only some of the great rivers that carve Africa into isolated segments. Only in the deserts of the Sahara and Kalahari does there seem to be a complete absence of water, and even there you can find it if you know where to look. It may be in the form of an oasis, surrounded by a tiny clump of palm trees, or it may actually be beneath the surface of the sands, so that unless you were taught the ways of the desert people you might easily die of thirst just a few inches away from as much water as you could possibly drink.

As a result of this diversity of land and climate the entire continent is populated by peoples living very different ways of life, so different that if they were moved from one environment to the other, they would die. They not only live differently—some of them hunting, some of them herding cattle, and others farming—but they are actually different people, speaking hundreds of languages, with as many customs and beliefs as well.

Some of them are as different in appearance as they are in culture. For instance, in North Africa the people may be as light or even lighter than some Europeans; in other parts of the continent they are almost black . . . and fiercely proud of it. In the east they are golden brown. In Ruanda Urundi you have some of the tallest people in the world—the Watusi—and living among them some of the smallest, the Pygmies.

So, just as it is true that there is no one African culture, so it is true that there is no one African race. There are Caucasians in the east and north, Negroes in the west, and in the east and south are the Bantu, who are probably a mixture of the other two. The Nilotics, who have spread from the Nile Valley on down into Uganda and Kenya, are a similar mixture, but because of strong Hamitic influences many of them are tall and slender and have long, straight features quite distinct from the Negroes'. The Pygmies of the Congo forests and the Bushmen of the Kalahari Desert are amongst the earliest inhabitants of Africa, but we are still unsure just what their relationship is, if any, to the African Negro. The Bushmen, in particular, seem very different in physique as in color.

There is no doubt that many of these physical differences are due to the environment, but we can not be sure exactly how they came about. One thing *is* sure, the fact that through evolution all animals, human beings included, have gradually developed the best equipment needed for effective survival in their particular environment. The color of the skin may well be a means of filtering out the harmful ingredients of strong sunlight; it may also have other functions. The tall, slender build of some of the Nilotic peoples, such as the Nuer and the Dinka, makes it possible for them to remain cool by providing them with a greater skin area in relation to their weight so that they can perspire more freely. In the constantly damp, cool rain forest there are no such needs, and the Pygmies are both lighter in color and stockier in build. And because they are so small it is much easier for them to move freely through their forest world in pursuit of game, following the trails made by the forest antelopes and buffaloes. The taller people are unhappy and uncomfortable in the forest; the Pygmies are miserable out of it. Each one of them has his own world, living his own way—and so it is throughout Africa.

The continent we know by the single name Africa, is in fact a number of totally different worlds, many of them isolated by geographical barriers and all of them as distinct both in terms of people and culture as they are in terms of the environment.

The history of Africa—as far back as we can trace it through the records of early explorers, through oral tradition, and through the findings of archaeologists—shows that there has been a constant movement of peoples from one area to another. This movement has been due largely to a steady growth in population, for when a population grows and the land on which it lives can no longer support it, at least a part of that population has to move elsewhere. This has meant a long history of conflict as well as of movement, for each successive wave of migrants forced the earlier inhabitants elsewhere, or else subjected them to domination.

Conflicts between traditional peoples, formed into nations or tribes, have generally been settled relatively easily because there has always been enough land. It meant, at the worst, that one tribe had to abandon its old land and move into new, and perhaps into a different type of environment, bringing a change to its accustomed way of life. New ways were learned, however, not only through people's moving from one environment to another, but by the meetings of many cultures brought about by this overall population movement. The Negroes, who may well have originated in West Africa, moved eastward and southward. The eastward movement crossed to the Nile Valley and there intermingled with a Caucasian people, notably with the Hamites of East Africa.

The southward movement pressed into the equatorial forest and on into the grasslands of East and South Africa. They too met other peoples, and through intermarriage became physically and culturally different from their West African ancestors. The inhabitants of this part of Africa are known collectively as Bantu because their languages all have the same characteristic use of prefixes, quite unlike other African languages.

Physically, the Bantu and the Nilotic are predominantly Negro, but they are not only different from each other; they are both different from the West African, sometimes referred to as the "true Negro." The people they displaced in the forest, the Pygmies, have many Negroid traits, but some scientists think of them as racially distinct because there are at least as many differences as there are similarities. The Bushmen, forced into the Kalahari by the southward expansion of the Bantu, once occupied vast areas of East Africa and are even more distinct racially, seemingly having little or no connection with the Negro and perhaps having a totally different origin.

Sometimes, when land was plentiful, the earlier inhabitants remained. Although in some cases they were held in subjection, in most cases they were assimilated by the incoming population, and there was an exchange of ideas leading to gradual acculturation. So tradition in Africa is certainly not a static thing. Tribal society has always been changing, growing, and adapting.

The greatest changes and conflicts of all have been brought from outside. We don't know when the first wave of migrants from the Middle East poured through the narrow neck of land connecting Africa to Asia, but it may have been many thousands of years before the Greeks and Phoenicians established their North African colonies about 1000 B.C.

All we know is that some five thousand years before the beginning of the Christian era the great Egyptian civilization was establishing its roots. This civilization drew its strength and character from both Africa and from the Middle East, as did the somewhat later Ethiopian civilization. But both were early centers of contact between Africa and the outside world, and through trade and military expansion along the Nile the early Egyptians had an enormous influence in East Africa, an influence that later spread even farther afield. Foreign influences became so strong in Egypt and Ethiopia that the African elements in their civilizations became almost completely obliterated by those from outside Africa.

The Roman invasion began in 146 B.C., and by the third century A.D. the whole of North Africa, from west to east, was under Roman domination; this much we know, and it is entirely possible that by this date both Greek and Roman influences had reached down either coast almost as far as the equator. On top of this came influences not only from India, but even from the Far East, and the east coast of Africa is rich in evidence of early contact with the Orient.

Before the major and most far-reaching invasion of all, that of the European colonists, there was yet another invasion—that of the Arabs. They had begun infiltrating in the north before the Romans, and had established trading posts down the east coast. But in the seventh century, following the death of Mohammed, there was an enormous influx of Moslem refugees and religious fanatics alike. One lot sought protection; the other sought to convert. Trading settlements moved inland from the coastal regions, and whole islands like Zanzibar were more or less taken over. The Arabs pushed all across the north coast of Africa. At its western limits some of them turned northward into Spain, others turned south and swept down, in the thirteenth century, to subject and convert the tribes of western Sudan. The Arab policy was to conquer one tribe, convert it, and move on to do the same to the next tribe, so that the Arab empire grew like a chain, link by link. They were in part fired by missionary zeal, forcing their belief in Islam upon the unbelievers at the point of the sword; but they were also driven by economic motives, in particular the trade in slaves and ivory. They made pacts with the chiefs of the local tribes, who ordered the hunting and killing of elephants, and then also compelled them to supply slaves to carry the ivory to the nearest port. On arrival there it was far better business to sell both the slaves and the ivory, and there were willing markets on both sides of the continent. Slaves were sold to the Orient from the east coast, and to the British, Portuguese, French, and Spanish settlements in the Americas from the west coast. A common belief of the time was that Africans were not human beings and thus they had no souls. Because of this convenient theory, there was no conscious immorality in the act of slavery.

Now, it is difficult to imagine how anyone could have ever genuinely believed this, but it has to be remembered that Africa was then a complete unknown to the western world. European knowledge of Africa was virtually nonexistent until the first Portuguese attempts to circumnavigate the continent in the fifteenth century.

Right up to the end of the nineteenth century, less than a hundred years ago, what little knowledge we had of Africa was confined to the coastal regions. The Portuguese and other mariners established posts all around the west, south, and east coasts of Africa to supply food and water for their ships traveling to and from India. But with the exception of the trading posts in South Africa, there was little attempt to move inland; for one thing, the nature of the countryside made transport difficult and dangerous.

But in the last quarter of the nineteenth century tne Industrial Revolution in Europe was making its effects felt far and wide. There was need to satisfy the ever-increasing demand for raw materials. An independent America was no longer a free source of supply, Asia had for some time been partitioned up, and now it was Africa's turn. So, in 1870 began the great "scramble for Africa" amongst the European powers, a scramble for the unknown economic resources of an unknown continent.

At this time slavery had already been abolished in the western world, but to the Europeans, in their ignorance of the ancient traditions of the African peoples, the dark-skinned, often nearly naked, tribesmen seemed savage indeed, with their incomprehensible customs.

In much the same spirit with which the British had colonized India, the various European powers in Africa taught the Africans that the road to success lay through as complete an imitation as possible of the European way of life and thought. They taught that traditional ways were barbaric and evil, and they reinforced their teaching by imposing heavy (and often truly barbaric) punishments for the continuance of certain customs. This was generally done in good faith, but it was not done with understanding. It was to be some time yet before the western world began to realize that it was destroying much of very real value in its attempt to modernize and westernize the African. It was to be some time before it acknowledged the simple fact that the mere lack of clothes was no measure of culture or civilization, and that prior to the advent of European powers, tribal society had codes of morality equivalent to their own, codes which tribal members kept rigidly. And it is only now that many of the Africans who have been taught to look away from their tribal past, are beginning to realize that they are on the point of letting knowledge of the past slip forever through their fingers. Already much tradition has been lost and can never be re-created.

One of the most remarkable things about the contact of African peoples with western civilization, however, has been the persistence of certain traditions and beliefs. The colonial powers did their best to bring to Africa an acceptance of the western way of life, and many Africans, particularly in the urban areas, have tried hard to adopt that way. In some cases there was no choice; for a man working in a mine hundreds of miles away from his family may find himself working alongside men of other tribes and perhaps with English as the only common language. Where cities grow up the tribal system breaks down completely; and even in the more remote areas where life is still lived much as it always has been, the mere fact that there is some authority higher than the traditional chief affects the whole working of the society. Apart from South Africa, one of the most highly westernized areas is the west coast. There the contact with Europe has been unbroken for some five hundred years, and the transition to western economy and western political systems has been gradual and steady. Even in the remotest village it would be rare to find nobody who could speak either English or French as well as his own language, and perhaps one or two others.

Along the coastal region there are great modern cities, where life is much like that in any European city, and where the Africans seem to be thoroughly westernized. Yet even there you find that some traditions die hard. Inland it is even more true, and despite the prohibition of certain customs and societies, the way of thought has not surrendered as easily as the way of life. People still find something of lasting value in the old way, something they are unwilling to give up merely to suit the new kind of clothes they are expected to wear, and the new kind of activities they are expected to perform.

Although we are here concerned with Africa and its peoples,

in learning about them and their problems there is a great deal we can learn about ourselves. In traditional African life, as in our own world, not so very long ago the family was a unit of extreme importance. It was important not only because of the great loyalty and affection between parents and their children, but because it was organized in such a way that this loyalty continued from birth to death, involving both responsibilities and privileges on each side. It was also organized on a somewhat larger scale than we generally think of.

We think of a family as consisting of a father and mother and their children. In African societies, usually, the children's children are also included, and the whole family of fathers and mothers, uncles and aunts, brothers, sisters, and cousins live close together, helping each other in the common concern for the provision of food and shelter. One member of the family helps another build his house or clear the brush for cultivation, just as one woman helps another hoe the fields. A hunter bringing back an antelope does not keep it for his wife and children alone, but divides it amongst those relatives who have been less fortunate. In times of shortage one relative can ask, and expect, help from another.

In short, in tribal society your concern is not for yourself as an individual, but for your whole family; and the tribe itself is built on this principle and thinks of itself as one single extended family, each member related to all others through common bonds of language, economy, and even of common blood, for at the head of the tribe stands the chief, often called "Father of the People," and often representing the original ancestor from whom all the members of the tribe are said to be descended.

It is not uncommon in Africa for one man to call another "Brother" even though there is no traceable relationship. But it is more than mere formality or politeness; it involves a feeling of mutual obligation and respect for one's fellow beings, and it may involve very heavy obligations should your "Brother" fall upon hard times. These obligations are all the harder to bear in a modern society where you live not by the food you plant, but by the money you earn in a mine or a store or even as the owner of a mine or a store. For the more money you have, the more will be the demands made upon you. But none the less, it is an obligation that many Africans are reluctant to abandon, as reluctant as they are to abandon the concept of the tribe or nation as being a family of men, women, and children all working for the common good.

This is only one of the aspects of tribal society that is in danger of being destroyed. There are many others of equal worth, perhaps of even more fundamental significance, and there are some that have already been irrevocably lost. But to understand them we have to try and forget our own customs for the moment, and we have to try not to judge the tribal African by comparing his ways with ours. Let us rather try and see the world as he sees it, for in many respects his world is different from ours. If we try and see it as he does, then customs that at first seem strange will fall into place, and a whole new and exciting world will be open to us.

THE BEGINNING OF MAN
IN AFRICA

We still are not sure where man as we know him today had his first beginnings. It is possible that he may have come into being in different places at roughly the same time, in the very distant past. But on the African continent there have been found some fossil remains of the very earliest of near-men. And also in Africa we have found remains of some of the even more ancient ancestral forms of animal life such as the little lemur-like creature that lived in Egypt 40 million years ago. It was already beginning to develop certain physical characteristics that later were to become the specific characteristics of the ape family.

Some of the man-types that have been found are far too recent to be our ancestors, as the little lemur might well be; such is the Australopithecus, or "southern ape," whose remains, found in South Africa, date back only about 500,000 years. Much like the apes and ourselves, these near-men were probably descended from the same common ancestor, but they were an offshoot that died off. An early man-type has yet to be found that is old enough to be the link between ourselves and that distant ancestor. Such a man-type may in fact have been found recently in East Africa, though as yet we do not know for sure. These remains, found by Dr. L. S. B. Leakey, seem to date back between one and two million years. It may be, however, that man had his beginnings elsewhere, and early on migrated in different directions, one group finding its way to Africa.

Some of the early men that we know lived on the continent differed significantly from each other, and as this was at a time when the continent was almost as geographically diverse as it is now, their differences may have been due to the different environments in which they were born and lived.

So from the earliest times there has been this diversity of peoples in Africa. And we also know, from the discoveries made by archaeologists and anthropologists, that for many thousands of years these early men provided themselves and their families in different ways with the food and shelter necessary for their survival. Some of these early ways, or economies, are still practiced today for the simple reason that without elaborate tools they are the only ways man can live in these particular environments.

In the tropical rain forest, for instance, the earliest men were hunters, and they still are today. It is impossible to keep cattle because there is no grazing land. In order to cultivate you have to have tools to cut down the huge trees—sometimes two hundred feet tall and the size of a small house at the base. Such a tree is hardly the kind you can chop down with a stone ax. So the only way to get food if you have only simple tools is by hunting for wild game, gathering wild fruits and vegetables, edible roots and nuts and mushrooms, and by fishing.

This is how the earliest man of all must have lived. Even before he learned to use a club or make a crude spear he probably went after game by watching the skies for vultures which guided him to newly dead animals.

In Africa today the vultures are still used as guides in areas of extreme hardship and shortage, and there are other ways in which men and animals work together for their mutual benefit. For instance, there is in East Africa a bird that knows where to find honey but can not get it away from the bees. So it comes fluttering around the camps of the hunters, diving and climbing, diving and climbing, until they see it and know that they are being called. They follow the bird and it guides them to the hive, probably deep in the bole of a tree. With fire and tools, the hunters smoke out the bees and chop away until there is a hole large enough for them to plunge their hands in and pull out the honey. They always leave some for the bird to encourage it to come to them again, and take the rest for themselves.

Early man in Africa must have learned all these tricks and many more, and much of what the Pygmy hunters of today know has been passed on down to them from father to son over many thousands of years. They still live on in the tropical rain forest, hunting and gathering as their ancestors did before them. Instead of stone tools, though, they use bows and arrows tipped with poison, and spears with metal blades forged by the neighboring tribes of cultivators.

The Pygmies are still hunters because they have never had the need to be otherwise—there has always been plenty of food all around them, and they are perfectly content. In fact, they think the cultivators stupid for working so hard.

A second group of hunters in Africa live in the Kalahari Desert, a very different environment. They are the Bushmen. And although their present homeland is very different from that of the forest Pygmies, their way of life is remarkably similar. They are in the desert not because it is their original home, but because they were driven there by other tribes, the cultivators who came down from the north and the Europeans who at the same time were pushing up from the south.

At one time or another the whole of Africa, from north to south, has been populated with hunters. There are great rock paintings in the Sahara Desert that show hunting scenes, telling us that the Sahara was not always the inhospitable barren region that it is today. But unlike the forest, which has always been lush and generous with its food supply, the Sahara gradually became less well watered. The animals that used to roam across its vast stretches died out, and the men who hunted them were forced to go elsewhere. But just about this time, between five and ten thousand years ago, man was beginning to learn two other ways of getting the food he needed: the herding of domesticated animals and cultivation of the soil.

This came about, probably, as the hunting land grew more and more arid. Men and animals alike searched for the few remaining sources of water. Perhaps they even competed for it, even though it is more in the nature of animals to go to the water in turn. There are parts of Africa today where you can see animals queuing up as though they were waiting for Noah's Ark, each kind of animal keeping to its own. They come down to the water in this way, one group of animals at a time. When they have drunk their fill they move on, and the next take their place. Antelopes, lions, buffaloes, elephants, leopards, all wait patiently and follow each other without argument when there is only the one source of life-giving water. Perhaps in this way, and in the way that the honey-bird and men still help each other today, certain animals first came to associate with men, moving about together in the common search for water, each allowing the other the chance to live.

In time the hunters disappeared completely from the North

African desert, but there are still peoples today who roam from one side to the other, driving their flocks of sheep and goats and camels from one meager pasture to the next. And when these people can not live by pastoralism, they live by trading, using the camel to carry them and their goods for thousands of miles. In this way the desert has never been completely uninhabited; from the early hunters onward there has been continuous movement across it, from east and west, north and south.

At the same time that man was learning to domesticate animals, perhaps in the Middle East, perhaps in the west of Africa also, man learned how to plant and reap certain crops: He became a farmer. This was a vitally important discovery, meaning a complete change in his habits. It may also have resulted in the further domestication of animals. In times of drought, when there was no pasture left, animals may well have fed on the husks of grain and on the straw thrown away by the farmers. And the farmers may have realized the usefulness of certain animals as beasts of burden, and of others as a source of food —breeding them and killing them in times of shortage or on special occasions, or else eating them when they died. And somewhere, at some time, man began to take milk from the cow and goat and use it for his own nourishment. Perhaps he only did this as a last resort in times of extreme hunger. Many cultivators in Africa today think of the milk of cows and goats as unclean, milk only being a food taken by babies from their mothers. But at the same time, often living right beside these cultivators, there are pastoral peoples who think of milk as the food most fit for a man.

In any case, the important thing is that hunters and gatherers were only able to survive in lush grasslands and in the tropical rain forest; elsewhere men had to take to herding cattle and farming, and this meant very different ways of living. The herders were still nomadic, wandering about much as they had when they were hunters, but instead of wandering in search of animals, they wandered constantly in search of fresh pastures. Their life was simple, and being nomadic, they could not acquire many material possessions. Nor did they need them. And so today the pastoralists of Africa live a simple, nomadic life, proud and independent.

But for the peoples who took to cultivation, both in the west and in the Nile Valley, it was different. They were not able to move so freely, for they had to stay to look after the crops they planted. Since they were more settled, they began to build more permanent dwellings; until then they had sheltered in caves or behind simple windbreaks made of branches and leaves or reeds. And, being more settled, they began to acquire possessions.

The presence of a permanent supply of water made life possible by means of cultivation, and this in turn made possible the building up of a surplus of food. The more crops that were planted, the richer the soil became, and the area under cultivation grew as did the size of the harvest. The Nile flooded annually, watering the entire valley, and as time went on, simple methods of irrigation developed into extremely ingenious systems. The result was an abundance of food that could be used for trade and as payment for labor.

The abundance also gave man time for relaxation and recreation. As a hunter or herder he had little opportunity for this, and particularly as a hunter he had to look for his food daily. But as a farmer he could store the grain he harvested and use it in lean times. Or he could use the excess grain to acquire other forms of wealth by exchange or to pay those who came to work his fields, thus giving him still more time to do other things.

This was combined with a steady growth in the size of the settlements. A hunting band or a group of nomadic pastoralists is never very large, simply because the supply of game or pasture land will not support large concentrations of men and animals. But the only restriction for the first farmers was the availability of suitable land, and the fertile Nile Valley stretched for hundreds of unknown miles, sparsely inhabited, into the distant south.

The Nile was more than a source of life to the soil, however, for the early farmers soon learned how to use it as a means of communication and trade, and as they began to look for more permanent materials with which to build their houses, they used it to transport stone from the southern quarries. The settlements grew into towns, even cities—cities that were not populated by farmers, but by specialists: craftsmen, workers in wood and metal, merchants, and government officials.

Government as we think of it was another outcome of man's discovery of farming. As long as he lived in small groups, there was no need for elaborate systems of authority. The father who was head of his family was, in general, the leader. But when man began to live in permanent settlements where many different families lived side by side, there had to be some more centralized form of control.

The original respect for the family, and the place of the family as the core of society, remained. But a much more elaborate superstructure was built up, like a pyramid. At the top of the pyramid, holding it all together, was the father of the land, the father of the people, the king or chief. Beneath him were his counselors, and beneath them were those to whom they delegated authority, and beneath them were the heads of important families who supervised their local groups, and at the base of the pyramid was the mass of the common people. The base and the apex were held together firmly by these links of family ties. When the community became so large that the sense of family loyalty was in danger of being lost, it was reinforced by the king's claiming direct descent from the original common ancestor of all, or, as in the case of the Egyptian Pharaohs, by claiming descent from the gods themselves. The king became divine, and there can be no argument with divine authority. In this way law and order were maintained in the ever-expanding agricultural centers, and today, thousands of years later, there are still "divine kingdoms" in both East and West Africa.

Well beyond the boundaries of ancient Egypt in the present Sudan, there live the Shilluk. They live, much as the early Egyptians did, strung along the banks of the river. They have some cattle, which graze the land between the settlements and the Nile, but the Shilluk are mainly cultivators. Their homes are on the high land set back from the river: about a hundred clusters of hillocks, each connected by a ridge, so that during the annual floods one hilltop is not isolated from the next.

On each hillock is a settlement, each settlement is divided into a number of hamlets, and each hamlet consists of a number of homesteads. The family system of control works at the homestead and hamlet level, and the leader of the settlement is elected by the headmen from amongst themselves. When he is elected his appointment is confirmed by the person to whom he is responsible—"the divine king."

Not much farther up the Nile live other tribes, such as the Dinka and the Nuer, who have no such centralization in the form of a divine king. Both are much more pastoral than the Shilluk, and they have to move their cattle around from one season to another. Also, their settlements are much more isolated and remote from each other than are those of the Shilluk.

We can see the same factors at work in West Africa, where intensive agriculture led to a development from small relatively isolated village communities into village clusters, and so into what can almost be called towns. This kind of development gives rise to the same kind of problems of authority, and in West Africa we also have "divine kingdoms." It also gives rise to the development of specialists, and with a royal court to encourage them and a surplus of food with which to pay them, it brings about a tremendous growth in arts and crafts. West Africa, just as was Egypt, is famous for the excellence of its wood- and metalwork, some of which is incomparable even by modern standards and techniques.

So we can see then, that civilization in Africa came about, as elsewhere, almost by accident. It was not a question of one people's being more intelligent or talented than another, it was largely a question of the stimulus they received from their environment. As long as they could continue to hunt and could live satisfactorily that way, they did so. Some still do, and although the present-day hunters have had contact with other African tribes of "civilized" cultivators, they want to have nothing to do with civilization. They look at it and do not see that it has anything to offer that they need and do not already have. A people's culture has to be judged not by how closely it resembles our own, but how well it is suited to its environment, human and geographical.

The term civilization refers literally to a city-state, at the least to a state that encourages urbanization and industrialization. But in its more general usage it implies a system of living where law and order are maintained with justice and equality, human conflicts both inside and outside the group are resolved with a minimum of violence, and where there is a moral code which people keep, more because they believe in it than because they are afraid of the consequences of breaking it.

In this sense, there are many African communities as fully civilized as our own, and among the most "civilized" in this sense are those who are the least civilized in the sense of being urbanized. For in terms of human relationships, it would be hard to find a more highly developed sense of respect, justice, and true morality than amongst those whom we often think of as being the more "primitive." Such are the hunters and gatherers with whom our story began, and whose descendants still live on in Africa today, following the ways of their ancient forefathers.

THE HUNTERS

We have been talking about the relationship between environment and culture, but there are other factors equally important. The environment *does* determine how we live, to a very great extent, until we learn how to control or modify it, but otherwise it merely makes certain ways of living possible and others impossible or very difficult. Obviously one can not grow crops in the middle of the desert or herd cattle in the middle of the forest. But there is no firmly fixed line. For example, hunters are found living in two of the greatest extremes in Africa, the Bushmen of the Kalahari Desert, and the Pygmies of the tropical rain forest.

Some people have maintained that the two peoples are related, but most evidence points toward the other direction. There are similarities between their cultures, however, which we can see by looking at them and comparing them. One of the most exciting things about the hunters is that in looking at them as they live today we are looking back into our own past.

The Bushmen are just about at the lowest possible level of subsistence. They perpetually face the danger of death from hunger or thirst; they have to wander continuously, seldom staying in one place for more than a day or two. Yet from all accounts they are one of the most human and humane of peoples.

They mostly live in the Kalahari Desert, in South West Africa, and they were driven there several hundred years ago by the tribes invading from the north and by the Europeans invading from the south. Caught in between these two hostile groups, the Bushmen had to leave the grassy plains and flee into the desert where nobody was willing to follow them. In the process many were slaughtered, and today only a few—perhaps forty thousand or so—survive. At one time they covered a much wider territory, and even in northeast Africa there have been archaeological discoveries indicating that a people very much like the present-day Bushmen once hunted there. They may once have lived still farther north, for some authorities see resemblances between the cave paintings of the Bushmen in South Africa and the paintings of the Sahara and even of southern Europe.

But this is all guesswork, and we are concerned with the Bushmen of today—the golden-brown, athletic little hunters who are only about five feet tall, but who can hunt down and kill any animal, however big or dangerous. With their thin bones and almost Mongolian-looking eyes, they look different from their neighbors and they know it; and they are proud of it because they are free.

Even though the desert is not their natural homeland, they have adapted to it in a remarkable way. It would be just about impossible for anyone else to live there, even with all the equipment and tools of modern civilization. Yet the Bushmen survive and refuse to leave. To leave would be to become the servants of others, and they prefer their freedom under the conditions of hardship they have to endure. The only alternative is for them to work for near-by farmers, white and black.

The desert is mile after mile of arid scrubland, with occasional tufts of thorn and clumps of grass, and every now and then a huge baobab tree standing up like a giant, two hundred feet into the scorching sky. Sometimes the scrub gives way to sand, sometimes to swamp. Within these thousands of square miles of harsh desert there wander small bands of Bushman hunters—perhaps only a few families in a band—each in its own territory.

They know the land well; every rise and fall of it, every clump of scrub, every tree, has a name. In the whole barren waste they are never lost, but always know exactly where they are. And where anyone else would think there was no food or water within a hundred miles or more a Bushman will walk a few feet to a little patch of scrub and pull out a *tsama* melon, or he will dig down into the sand with a hollow reed that he always carries with him, and begin to suck. He may have to suck so hard and so long that his lips get bruised and bleed, but he knows that water is there, and in time it comes up through the reed, enough not only to slake his thirst, but perhaps enough to fill the shell of an ostrich egg.

These shells are carried on long trips across the more barren reaches of the desert, and it is a sign of their trust in their fellow creatures that Bushmen will bury shells full of water beneath the sand with no fear of their being stolen. This provides a supply of water while they travel or hunt in a particular area. The code of the Bushmen is simple but strict, and in matters concerning food and water it is particularly strict. So much so, that if a Bushman were dying of thirst and he came across a cache of eggshells, it is doubtful that he would take them to save himself. For by saving himself in this way he knows that other Bushmen, relying on the fact that water should be there, would find none and might die.

Consideration for his fellows extends right through his whole life. A family is close and intimate, but a Bushman will not ignore the needs of others merely because they are not his kin. If there is food for one, there is food for all, and there is only one occasion on which the rule does not apply. When men and women get old they are unable to hunt as they used to, and they have to stay behind as the others go daily in search of food. This is accepted, and they are gladly cared for by their children with affection. Usually they die before they become totally inactive, but sometimes they live on to the point where they just can not keep up with the others as they wander on endlessly from one part of the desert to the other. If the band does not move, the members starve; for if they stay in any one place too long they eat up all the melons and edible roots near-by and hunt out all the game. If anyone is incapable of following them as they move on, there is only one thing to do: leave them behind.

For a people as loyal and as devoted as the Bushmen this must be a terrible moment, but it can not be avoided, and the old people know it as well as their children. A shelter is built, and the old person is given whatever food and water can be spared, and with much weeping he is left to his fate. He may die of heat exhaustion or starvation, but more likely he will be attacked and killed by wild animals. The Bushmen will never abandon their old until there is no other hope—only when the whole band is on the point of starvation. But when it has to be done, the old accept their fate without a word of complaint.

This consideration for life is even extended to the animal world. Because he is a hunter does not mean that the Bushman enjoys killing. He kills only because he has to, in order to live. So he only kills when necessary, never for fun, never with any pleasure in the actual killing—rather with compassion. And when he has killed he is not wasteful of any part of the dead animal that can possibly be used, if not for food then for clothing or some other use, such as the making of skin pouches and arrow quivers, or gut twine. He has to do this because the hunting is not always good, and the maximum use has to be made of any kill. It may take days to hunt a single animal; three or four men, with their bows and arrows or spears, steadily run their quarry down, using their skill and intelligence to tire it out before they themselves tire. When there is a kill followed by a short time of plenty, although the Bushmen do not gloat over the dead animal, they do not forget to offer their thanks to the spirit that they believe watches over them. It is both an act of thanks and an act of propitiation for having destroyed another fellow creature.

To the Bushman the whole world is alive and part of the same great creation—not only the human beings, but also the animals and the birds and the insects, the plants and the trees, the hills and the sands. They are a part of his life, and he is a part of theirs, and although Bushmen do not have a formal religion as we think of it, they are essentially religious.

The hunting peoples of Africa have less magic and witchcraft than any others, and they have no sorcery. Sorcery is an act of evil, a deliberate, conscious willing of evil by one human being upon another. To the hunters, with their respect for life in all its forms, this is incomprehensible. Evil in that sense simply does not exist. Even magic and witchcraft are not what they are elsewhere, but are closer to the acts of faith than anything else. For the belief of the Bushmen is that the Great First Spirit will look after them, and if it wills that they die, then they accept death calmly, without complaint. They have to kill in order to live, so they see no reason for complaining when the time comes for them to die. In times of bad hunting, or when there is no sign of the rain that gives a spark of life to the arid ground and brings forth the melons and other foods they depend on, then the Bushmen will dance a rain dance, drawing the attention of the First Spirit to their plight. Similarly, when someone is ill and there is no effective medicine to cure him, they will dance. But again, it is more an act of faith than it is of magic, for they do not believe that they have the power themselves, merely that there *is* such a power, and that it will heed them.

Every day the men go off to hunt and the women and children go off to search for whatever growing thing that can be eaten, be it fruit or root. They often return too exhausted to do anything but sleep, but at other times they gather together and sing and dance. This act of singing and dancing is both a recreation and an expression of their joy. They dance under the open sky and they sing to the stars which, they say, are hunters like themselves, chasing their quarry across the sky. For to them hunting is the only really worthwhile way of living, not only in their world of the Kalahari but in the entire universe. It is this belief that holds them together and gives them the strength they need to survive.

Like the Bushmen in many ways, though physically very different, are the forest Pygmies. Even shorter, they average between four and four and a half feet in height. Although they do not have the Oriental look of some Bushmen, and in fact look much more like other Africans, they too are light in color, having a reddish-yellow skin. The Bushmen have a strange eye-fold and high cheekbones quite unlike other African peoples; the Pygmies have neither of these characteristics, but their eyes are set farther apart than those of the true Negro, and their noses are much broader. Their blood type also seems significantly different from that of the Negro. They have rather stocky bodies, with relatively short legs, but they are extremely powerful. Perhaps because they are so active, like the Bushmen, they generally keep in excellent health.

Like the Bushmen, the Pygmies, or BaMbuti as they are called in the northeast Congo, live a simple life, hunting and gathering almost daily. Their organization is equally simple. Not living in large groups like the cultivators, and having plenty of land in which to hunt without one band coming into conflict with another, they do not need an elaborate system of government. There are no chiefs, and any questions or disputes are settled by general discussion in which everyone takes part. Also, like the Bushmen, the hunting bands tend to be family units, and the oldest father or grandfather is given considerable respect and has some authority.

But the forest is a much kinder world to the hunters than is the desert. It shelters the BaMbuti from the heat of the sun, it provides them with fresh drinking water wherever they go, and it supplies an abundance of game and vegetable foods. There is no great problem in securing the food for the day, and sometimes a hunt will be successful enough to make it possible for the entire band to relax for the following day or two. During this time they will sing and dance, much like the Bushmen, and they will do odd chores such as making more bows and arrows or spears, mending their hunting nets, adding to their leaf huts, or making the bark cloth they wear.

The Pygmies, like the Bushmen, are nomadic, for even though the game here is much more plentiful than it is in the Kalahari Desert, it still tends to move away to another part of the forest if a hunting band stays in one camp too long. Also, the women find after a few weeks that they have to go too far away to gather the roots, mushrooms, nuts, and berries they like. So generally a camp in the forest will only last about a month.

The huts are built of small saplings, stuck in the ground and bent over to form a sort of igloo-shaped frame. This is hung with huge, heavy leaves, like tiles, and it is both warm and waterproof. It does not take long to build, so when a camp is abandoned all the huts are left behind to rot. The Pygmies have few enough possessions, though probably more than most Bushmen, but they can never own more than they can carry on their backs.

Some Pygmies use only the bow and arrow or the spear for the hunt. They live in small bands, perhaps of only three or four families, and in the mornings the men go off together to find fresh animal trails. They climb up into trees and wait for the animals to pass, sometimes calling them by imitating their cries. Then they simply shoot them with their arrows, or spear them. There is no need to build elaborate traps or to dig pits. While they are hunting, the women and children go in search of other food. Strangely enough, perhaps because there is so much game, there is practically no fishing except by the small children.

But there are other groups of Pygmies who hunt with nets and who tend to live in much larger bands, perhaps of twenty or more families. Yet even in these larger bands there are no chiefs, everything being decided by mutual consent after general discussion. Usually the men will discuss where to hunt the next day, but the women are perfectly free to join in, and they frequently do, telling the men that a given area has no mushrooms and other delicacies, that it would be better to go elsewhere, where the hunting and gathering could be combined.

Sometimes there is disagreement, and it can blow up into a noisy argument. But just about when it looks as though it might be developing into a fight, someone, usually an old man or woman, will wander casually in between the quarrelers and tell them they are making too much noise. He will say that if they continue like that, they will scare all the animals away and then everyone will go hungry. This is good reasoning, and the quarrel will stop. By the next morning it will have been forgotten, for the thought of an empty stomach makes any dispute seem insignificant.

Early in the morning, before it is properly light, the camp comes to life. Each tiny leaf hut has its own fire, which is kept inside at night. This is now brought out and put in front of the door. In the always-damp forest the nights and early mornings can seem bitterly cold, though the temperature never drops below 70 degrees. There may be a central fire, and the men will cluster around this, hugging themselves to keep warm. They drink a brew of forest berries and herbs, and while their wives are preparing a simple breakfast, they stretch out their nets and make sure that they are intact. Then they carefully coil them over their shoulders, letting each coil hang almost to the ground so that the net can be carried easily and unwound quickly without snagging.

After breakfast the men and women both set off. A few youths go first and light a fire under a tree as an act of propitiation, and as a sign to the Spirit of the Forest that its children, as they call themselves, are going to hunt. Like the Bushmen, the Pygmy hunters have a strong belief in the existence of a benevolent spirit. They do not know what it is or what it looks like or where it lives, but they feel that there must be such a spirit which constantly looks after them. The Pygmies generally refer to it simply as the "forest" itself, for it is the obvious source of all life; it is the all-provider. Or sometimes they call the forest

"Mother" or "Father," and refer to themselves as its children. For like their real father and mother, they say, the forest gives them food and warmth, clothing and shelter . . . and, they add, affection.

A net hunt may bring in several antelopes at one try. The men all stretch out their nets, end to end in a great semicircle, and the women and children form a semicircle facing it. At a given signal they start beating in toward the nets, whooping and shouting, and beating at the undergrowth with branches. The animals are driven into the nets and are quickly killed by the men with their spears. Sometimes an antelope will jump right over the net if it sees it in time, or else it may escape around the edge. Then the young boys, not yet old enough to have nets of their own, will try to catch it with their hands. And as soon as enough animals have been caught, everyone returns, shouting and singing, to camp.

The game is divided up so that nobody goes without, and special preference is given to the old people who can no longer hunt for themselves. While hunting, the women will have been gathering mushrooms, the sweet *itaba* root, and whatever nuts they can find, and these will all be used in cooking the evening meal. During the hunt they may have a quick snack of fruits or berries, or of some prepared food brought along with them, but they have only two main meals each day. Nearly all their food is cooked over open fires, the meat impaled on sticks, with roots and nuts roasted in the ashes. There are no alcoholic drinks, but on cold mornings or evenings a stimulating concoction of berries, herbs, and nuts is brewed and drunk from leaf containers.

By sundown the meal has been eaten, and in the darkness the fires outside each hut burn brightly. At this time the men may gather together with the women, or separately, and sit around and talk, telling stories of the great hunts they have been on and of the exploits of their fathers and of their fathers before them.

Storytelling is a favorite pastime, and sometimes a storyteller will get so worked up that he will stand up and start stamping the ground, throwing his arms about and dancing in imitation of the hunt he is describing. If he is particularly good, the others will all clap their hands and sing a chorus, or they too will stand up and dance around the fire. Like the dance of the Bushmen, this is more than fun; it is an expression of the sheer joy they feel in the completeness of their life, and there is no sight in the whole of Africa that is more impressive, to me at any rate, than this firelight dance of the hunters. The glowing firelight casts shadows of gigantic Pygmies dancing across the forest floor and up into the leafy roof overhead, and the rich vibrant singing echoes back from the darkness all around as a reminder that the Pygmies are not only full of joy, but also full of faith.

There is a belief in the forest that if there is any serious crisis, there is no need to do anything but sing. There are special songs for these occasions, quite different from other songs, and they are sung by the firelight at nighttime. They may be sung right through the night, almost until dawn, and for night after night. There are few words to the songs, sometimes none, but what words there may be are no more than expressions of faith: "The forest is good," "the forest is kind." For the Pygmies believe that crises can come only because the forest is sleeping and is not aware of what is happening to its children. All they have to do, the Pygmies say, is sing to it to wake it up.

And among themselves their trust is equally great. Theft is considered one of the greatest of all crimes, but it is so rare that there is no special punishment for it. In fact, it is characteristic

of these African hunters that there is virtually no formal law
and no system of punishment. There is certainly nothing like
a police force. It is accepted that a man or a woman will behave
in a certain way—the way their fathers and mothers behaved
and taught them, the way they teach their children. There may
be petty squabbles and jealousies, but they are forgotten
as quickly and as easily as they blow up.

With so few possessions, there is little temptation to steal;
the greater temptation, perhaps, is to be lazy. This is frowned
on, but instead of punishing a lazy person, the Pygmies simply
laugh at him. There is generally a clown in every band, and in
the evening when the families are all gathered together he will
make merciless fun of the lazy offender. The Pygmies are
a proud people, and they are quick to take offense at personal
slights of this kind, so this is generally enough to bring a man
to his senses. If it does not, then the ridicule will be intensified,
and throughout the day men, women, and children alike will
make fun of the lazy party, but I have seldom seen it go as far
as this.

The same system works for other "crimes," so there is no need
for courts, juries, and judges. But there *is* always the threat of
exile. The Pygmies say that if anyone did commit a really terrible crime such as theft or adultery, then he would be turned
out of the camp to live alone in the forest. No other band would
take such a person in, and as it is impossible to survive alone
in the forest, the culprit would die. He would not die from
attack by wild animals, but rather from starvation, because it
is just about impossible to hunt successfully alone, and in any
case he would have no fire with which to cook his food.

Many people think of the forest as being dangerous, but in
fact it is nothing of the sort. It may be filled with some of the

most dangerous animals and snakes in the world, but they are only dangerous to those who do not understand their ways or to those who intentionally court danger. When the men and women go off in the morning to hunt, the camp is deserted except for one or two old people, perhaps, and the young children who choose to stay behind and play. And as the old people do not like to be disturbed all the time by their grandchildren, there is generally a small clearing, apart from the main camp, where the youngsters spend their time. They splash in the stream, they climb to the tops of young saplings, bending them down to the ground and jumping off to watch the sapling shoot upright again, or else they swing in long vine swings, hanging from branches perhaps a hundred feet above.

In these *bopi,* as they are called, the children play alone, with nobody to supervise. In the main camp the old people stretch out on the ground, fastidiously using leaves as mats, and sleep in peace. Not once have I ever heard of any harm coming as a result of this trust the Pygmies have in the world around them. Even in the heart of the forest, miles away from the camp, there is no great danger . . . except possibly if you are too quiet. For if you make no noise, you may well stumble across a dozing buffalo or leopard or tread on an unwary snake. So Pygmies almost always travel in numbers, and as they travel through the forest they shout and sing and make as much noise as possible. Only when they are actually hunting are they silent.

Perhaps we can see the vague beginnings of a more formal organization among the net-hunting Pygmies, for unlike those who only use bow and arrow, and unlike the Bushmen, the Pygmies often form quite sizable hunting bands of up to thirty families. These families may not all be directly related to each other, so that there is no one man who can call himself father of the band. Also, unlike the Bushmen, the Pygmy net-hunters tend to stay in one place for a much longer time, and so they build more permanent camps.

Whereas a Bushman hut is little more than a windbreak— just a few sticks stuck in the ground with some brush or scrub thrown across—a Pygmy hut is a relatively elaborate affair. It is completely covered with leaves, with only a small opening left as a door. There is complete privacy inside. If the family is large, an extension may be built on it for the children, and sometimes if a man has two wives (though this is not common among the Pygmies) each will build her own hut, joined or not according to how well the wives get on with each other. When a man has a number of relatives living with him, and Pygmies love visiting each other, his wife may build on several extensions, all joining one another.

This kind of community, particularly one where there is a great deal of change through people's coming and going on visits, and where the hunters belong to several different families, loyalty can not be on the simple family-level basis that prevails among the Bushmen. The hunting band may think of itself as a family, but the biological bonds are not there. They try, however, to create them by using the same terms of address for relatives and others. Anyone of your own age you call brother or sister; anyone older, you call father, mother, or grandparent. Anyone younger is called child. And it goes beyond just calling someone by this name. If you call someone father, then you have certain rights, and can expect him to treat you as your own father does. But at the same time you have corresponding responsibilities, and when he gets old, he can expect you to help feed him as you would your real father.

So the illusion of a family is maintained, and instead of having a single person giving judgment and making decisions by virtue of his being the head of the family, you have all the various family members taking part in any discussion. But even so, there is more cause for friction and jealousy in this kind of a group than there is in the smaller one-family band. And the longer a large group hunts together and moves about the forest together, the worse these jealousies become.

The difficulty is solved partly by the accepted pattern of one family's deciding to leave for a time and going to visit another hunting band, but more particularly by the complete change in the usual pattern of life that comes about in the honey season. This is the one season that the Pygmies know, for otherwise the forest is much the same the year round. It rains all year, with slightly less rain at one time (from December to January), but not enough to make much difference to the game or the plant life. And since the forest is equatorial, the temperature is even all year. But once a year, for two months or so—in June and July—the honey season comes. Honey is the Pygmies' major source of sugar, and it is the one food they prize above all others. The honey season, then, is a time for rejoicing and merrymaking, and as it is also a time when the vegetables, fruits, and mushrooms are if anything more abundant than other times, the hunt is almost abandoned.

This means a complete breakup of the hunting group. Before the season it was held together because the cooperation of all the men, women, and children was necessary in order to hunt effectively with nets. So when the hunt is no longer important, this common bond is removed. Honey is something that is hunted individually, not together, so each man goes off on his own in search of a honey tree that he then marks as his own; nobody else will touch it. And since the Pygmies, like the Bushmen, have a large territory at their disposal, each hunting band tends to break up and disperse over the entire area in small family units.

This is a time then, once a year, when real family ties are strengthened and reaffirmed among the net-hunters. Two or three brothers go off together, each with their wives and children, and their parents if they are still living. Together, they make a small camp near their honey trees, and there they stay for most of the honey season. If they invite a stranger with them, it is a sign of extreme friendship, a bond almost as strong as that of kinship.

Pygmy hunter

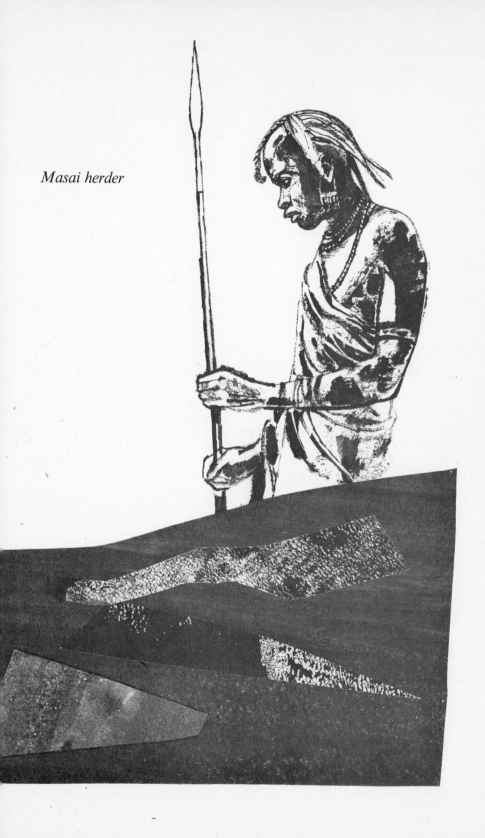

Masai herder

During the day the men go off with their bows and arrows and spears, one of them carrying a burning brand of fire. The Pygmies do not know how to make fire, but have to keep it burning at all times. They probably got it in the first place from a fire started by lightning, and it is cherished almost as a sacred possession. When they get to the tree with the hive in its bole, they climb up, thrust the burning embers inside, much as do the Bushmen, and then pull out the honey and put it into the leaf-lined baskets slung on their backs. They eat a great deal of it on the spot, bringing the rest back to the camp to share with the others. Maybe on the way they may kill an animal or a bird with bow and arrow; if not, they simply eat the honey and whatever vegetables and roots their wives have managed to find. Then in the evening they gather their families together and everyone sings the special honey songs that are only sung at this time of year, or dance the honey dance, the men imitating the hunter as the women imitate the bees. Like the rest of their music, the honey songs are all vocal except for a pair of wooden clappers; there are no other instruments.

Toward the end of the honey season, however, these little family groups begin to feel lonely and miss the companionship of the larger camp. They also begin to long for the excitement of the net hunt and for the meat. So they gradually move closer together, and re-form into a larger net-hunting band. It may or may not be as it was before; in fact, it will almost certainly be different. Certain families who had special grievances will make this an opportunity for going elsewhere without causing any offense. The others will rejoin each other with a renewed sense of family loyalty and a new-found enthusiasm and friendship for the rest of the camp. The small jealousies and hostilities of the previous year will have been forgotten or removed, and in the common desire to resume the communal hunt the old bonds will be forged anew.

It is almost as though the forest hunters were aware that if they allowed the large group to get too settled, they would have to find some more formal way of ordering its activities. It is against the nature of the hunter to give orders or to take them, for every man and woman is a man or woman enjoying full equality with the others, and is expected to be equally responsible.

There is no competition to outdo the next person, because there is no reward in the way of personal gain or increase in personal status. So there is no one person better fitted than the others to be a chief, and there are few who would want to take on the responsibility of trying to maintain order on his own authority. It is also against the nature of the hunter to inflict punishment. If there is any punishment such as ridicule or exile, it is inflicted by the whole group together. So, when a group gets too large and unwieldy, when there are too many problems, even if it is not yet the honey season, it just tends to split up, each part going its own way.

In recent years the forest has been getting smaller, in the sense that the Europeans were putting roads through the Ituri, that part of it which was the last refuge for the true hunting-and-gathering Pygmy. The roads restricted the movement of game, and this in turn restricted the movements of the Pygmies. Also, an increasing number of cultivators have for many years been pressing into the forest home of the hunters, cutting down the trees to make their plantations. With these people the Pygmies came to terms, exchanging any surplus of meat, forest fruits and nuts, and the leaves and saplings villagers use to build their houses, for the plantation foods, such as bananas and rice, of the villagers. But any attempt on the part of the villagers to establish more formal relationships have been resisted with sly cunning.

A band of Pygmies will seem to enter into a kind of trade agreement with one village and will even adopt some of the village customs and perhaps the village language. If you were to see them in the village, where they may stay for several days, weeks, or even longer periods of time, you might think they were completely under village control. You might also think they had a chief of their own who represented them in discussions with the village chief. But this is all superficial.

The Pygmies are jealous about their forest, and they do not readily allow foreigners into it, whether they are villagers or Europeans. But if you were lucky enough to be able to go with them when they return to the forest after they have satisfied their curiosity and spent as long as they want in the village, eating village food and maybe doing a little work in return, then you would see the change come over them.

One evening they will get together in their own corner of the village—they never live right in it amongst the villagers, but usually camp on one edge, between the village and the forest. They will decide that there is nothing to be gained by staying any longer, and they will pack their few belongings into their vine baskets, and early the next morning they will slip out, trekking through the plantation, silent until they reach its edge and enter the forest by some almost invisible trail.

Once they are in its protective shade, they become different people. They start laughing and joking, telling each other of the good time they have had, making fun of the villagers who have been feeding them for the past days in the hopes of getting more labor and meat out of them. Then, as they get deeper in the forest, they start singing. Perhaps someone will shout to the forest, calling it father or mother, asking it how it is, saying that they are glad to be back. A great chorus of song will burst from the others, and each person in turn will shout or sing his greeting in this way.

Once they are well away from the village, perhaps a whole day's march away, they build a camp and at night gather around a central fire to sing their songs of praise. The village and its ways are all but forgotten, the Pygmies no longer behave as they did, for they only did so to please the villagers. Here they are in their own home, and they are themselves, for they will never sing their great forest songs in the village; there is always some part of their forest life that remains behind when they bring meat down to the plantations. Equally they want to keep the village out of the forest, so they tell the villagers all manner of stories about how dangerous the forest is, full of wild animals and dangerous evil spirits, with the result that nearly all villagers have a hearty mistrust of the forest world and prefer to leave it to the Pygmies.

And sometimes, during the sacred *molimo* festival, as they are singing their great songs of devotion far into the night, one of the older Pygmies gets up and slowly wanders over to the edge of the camp where the trail leads to the distant village. It is rather like someone feeling a draft and getting up to close the door. He stares into the forest for a while, down the trail; then he finds a fallen branch or log, and pulls it over, letting it fall across the path, shutting off the outside world more completely. For the forest is the home of the Pygmies, they say, and no place for savages and strangers, be they white or black, who seek to cut it down and destroy it.

THE PASTORALISTS

The Bushmen and the Pygmies are the only two major groups of hunters left in Africa. Elsewhere this early form of life has given way to the more complex economies such as the herding of cattle and the growing of crops. We don't know which came first, or if both these later forms came together, but although there are plenty of African cultivators who keep no cattle, there are only a few herders who still refuse to grow any crops. But there are some. Their nomadic existence makes it difficult or impossible to tend cultivated fields, and many of them despise the cultivators as inferior peoples.

Pastoralism is the way of life spread right across North Africa and down the east coast until the area which bulges in from the coast to cover almost the entire central region and is plagued with the tsetse fly, in which the cattle die off. Below this tsetse belt, in South Africa, there is more pastoralism.

It seems that the herding and general domestication of animals had its major start in North Africa. Perhaps the Negro tribes who migrated across the southern fringe of the desert brought it with them, or perhaps they were cultivators who came across the pastoral way of life during their wanderings.

Anyway, along the part of the Nile that flows through the Sudan there are a number of Negroid tribes, often called Nilotics, whose life today is still centered around pastoralism. They are tall and slender, dark in color, and their proud temperament shows in the way they carry themselves—with grace, dignity, and no little arrogance. Some of them have more cattle and less agriculture than others, and this seems to depend largely on the nature of the countryside. In fact, these Nilotics adapt themselves so completely to their environment that although their cultures are basically similar, the end result is different in each case.

The three main tribes of Nilotic pastoralists—the Shilluk, the Nuer, and the Dinka—all live close to each other. Nevertheless, while the Shilluk not only have chiefs but also a "divine king," the other two do not even have any chiefs. And while the Shilluk live in permanent villages all year round, the Nuer abandon their villages totally during the dry season, and the Dinka fall somewhere in between the two, their villages being occupied by at least a few people all year round while the others wander about with the cattle.

The Shilluk people have fewer cattle than most other Nilotic peoples, and they live along a stretch of the river where there is a string of about a hundred connected hills not far from the river banks. Between these hills and the river there is good pasture land, enough for the cattle all year round. Each hill forms a settlement that is part of the Shilluk nation, with its own representative to the central court. Each settlement is divided into small hamlets consisting of a number of related homesteads. The family is still an important unit, because it is the heads of families who elect the settlement representative.

These hundred settlements—each with a population of a

thousand or so (very dense for this region)—are strung in a line along one bank of the Nile, and the kingdom is divided into two halves, north and south, with the capital, Fashoda, in the middle. If the villages were all isolated and had no direct connection with each other, each farming its own land and looking after its own cattle, there would be no feeling of belonging to a nation. But with several homesteads linked together by family ties, and these clusters of homesteads linked together by a common, elected representative, and the common representatives linked together by the fact that they belong to the northern or

Shilluk

to the southern half of the kingdom, the Shilluk peoples are very strongly united indeed.

This is important for them, because in the past they have had to guard themselves against attack from other pastoral peoples who would have liked to overrun Shilluk land so that they could expand. No one family could have stood up on its own against such invaders. The strong division of the kingdom into two halves protected it from both possible directions of attack, north and south. The position of the king was simply to act as a symbol of the unity of the nation, and to balance the two halves of the nation so that they did not fall out with each other. It was not that he as an individual was of any particular importance; the important thing was the idea that he stood for, and he was held to represent the original founding ancestor, Nyikang, from whom the Shilluk are legendarily descended. He is the center of the ritual life of the nation, and upon him its prosperity depends. It is almost as though the Pygmies were to elect one of their hunters to represent the forest in order to constantly be reminded, by his presence, of the whole source of their existence. If the Shilluk king betrayed his trust in any way—by favoritism or by not fulfilling his ritual role—he was replaced by another.

Just to the south of the Shilluk are the Nuer, who spill over on both sides of the Nile. They are an extremely powerful nation who have at one time or another attempted to spread out into the land occupied by their neighbors. In terms of force of arms—clubs and spears—they could probably have succeeded, but they were forced to retreat to their own land because all around them the country was just different enough to make it impossible for them to live their accustomed way. They could have adapted themselves, but they did not want to, preferring instead to continue in the manner of their fathers and forefathers.

The Nuer live for part of the year much as the Shilluk do, on hilltops close to the banks of the Nile. But their hills are isolated from each other; they are not connected by ridges and are much farther apart. As a result, when once a year the rains come and the Nile floods, the flat land all around becomes covered with water, and each hilltop village is completely cut off from the next except by canoe—and sometimes the nearest village may be twenty miles away. At this time of year all the cattle are gathered up into the village, where special byres are built for them with fires kept burning to keep away the flies and mosquitoes. Young men tend them constantly and live in the byres with the cattle.

But during the dry season everyone moves. Unlike the land of the Shilluk, there is no pasture here at all between the villages and the river; the nearest pasture may be fifty or a hundred miles inland. A number of villages which form a natural cluster then combine and drive their cattle to these inland dry-season pastures. It is during this time of year that one lot of villagers are able to meet the others, renewing old friendships, forming new. This also is a time for young people to become betrothed. At the dances in cattle camps boys and girls form attachments with each other, then seek their parents' approval. A marriage is not only a personal affair, for it affects the economy of the whole community, and the whole community is involved in the protracted ceremony. At the end of the dry season there is another migration back to the villages, and once again communication is almost cut off.

Again it is plain that the individual family is a very important unit, but that a sense of nationhood can not be felt as it is by the Shilluk. Yet the Nuer, just like the Shilluk or any other pastoral peoples, are constantly in danger of being invaded by others seeking fresh pastures, and they themselves would like to expand their own territory. So to get some kind of unity that reaches farther than the village, they form themselves into territorial units divided by rivers and streams.

A number of these units think of themselves as all being part of the same large family descended from a single common ancestor of long ago—the tribe. It is made up of a number of families who can actually trace their relationship, and these generally are the groups that live and work together and have most to do with each other. But if there is any threat from outside, then all the families join together as one huge family.

This was not true of the hunters because the land they live on supports them; they do not need to take land that belongs to others. So among the Pygmies and Bushmen, whole tribes do not unite, one against the other; each family band keeps to itself except when a family pays a social visit to another group. But with the pastoralists the family sense in itself is insufficient. It is not enough that each individual family should be prepared to fight for its own little plot of land; if they did this, they would be quickly destroyed. So there has to be some way of getting men, particularly the young ones who will do the fighting, to form a group regardless of their actual family ties.

Thus, groups of men are formed according to age rather than by family relationships. Every few years there are a series of initiations during which all uninitiated youths are cut across the forehead as a sign that they are now men. For the rest of their lives they will carry the marks as a proof of their courage and their fitness to take on adult responsibilities. From then on they will think of all those initiated at the same time as brothers, forming a distinct group called an age set, fighting together as a regiment.

But these age sets are not only for warfare. Warfare is sometimes a necessity if the tribe is to survive, but the most important thing in the lives of the Nuer and other pastoralists is the preservation of their cattle. The tribes along the banks of the Nile all practice a certain amount of cultivation, and even with them the cattle are their main concern. But there are those who moved farther south in the search of fresh pasture land, and some of these gave up farming for one reason or another and now rely almost entirely on their cattle for food and clothing. The hides are worn as capes around the shoulders, but the cattle are rarely killed for this purpose or even to provide meat except on ritual occasions. At other times the milk is drunk, often mixed with blood drawn daily from the jugular veins of cows.

These people have been given a reputation of being fierce fighters, constantly at war. The tribe that certainly had the worst reputation in this respect is the Masai, who now stretch through Kenya and Tanganyika. The young men form an age set in much the same way as the Nuer youths, having to prove their courage and strength before they are given the responsibilities of manhood. For if you live this kind of life, you have to be strong to be an adult. No father would want to give his daughter to a man who could not defend her and who could not provide her with food. So no man can be married until he has proven himself.

If the Masai learn to be great fighters, as they certainly are, it is as with other pastoralists, primarily because they have to be courageous and even fierce to defend their cattle from the lions and leopards that constantly threaten them. The term for young man—*Ol Morane*—rather than meaning "warrior" as it is often translated, means "protector of the cattle," which in

turn really means "protector of life." This is very different from
what we think of when we say "warrior," and it is just one
example of how much we have misunderstood the traditional
life of the peoples of Africa.

The Masai, in spite of plenty of opportunity, and although
they have seen enough of western civilization to understand
what it has to offer, refuse to abandon their traditional way of
life. In the course of their wanderings down into their present
homeland they have come to depend entirely on their cattle.
With something of the respect that the hunter feels for the ani-

62

mals he has to kill in order to survive, the Masai respect the
cattle that give them life. Perhaps this is why they have survived
when others have been defeated or forced to abandon their old
ways.

From the moment of birth the Masai are taught to respect
cattle. They are taught to refer to their cows and oxen as sister
and brother, and they feel the same kind of obligation to the
animals that they would to their own family. It is nothing for a
Masai literally to defend a single cow, with his own life, against
a marauding lion or leopard. In our own society we think of

the shepherd, who does the same thing for his sheep, as a symbol of goodness and peace. The Masai is much closer to the shepherd than he is to our idea of a warrior, and if he is fierce at times, it is because he has to be fierce to be able to drive off wild animals with no more than a spear or club or even his bare hands. If he is fierce toward other human beings, it is only when they threaten to deprive him of his chosen way of life.

So strong is the feeling for cattle that some pastoral peoples identify themselves with them. They may bind the horns of the ox so that they grow curved into strange shapes, and at the same time bind their own wrists tightly so that for a few weeks they will be deformed as are the horns of their oxen. They believe that their future both in this life and the next are inextricably bound together. Obviously then, when these peoples come in contact with those who have no cattle, there is some conflict.

The pastoralists who pushed down into East Africa from the north came into a land already occupied by groups of cultivators who had no cattle. The cultivators felt as strongly about their land as the pastoralists did about their cattle and were equally prepared to defend it. But usually the pastoralists, who had to live a more vigorous life, were the better fighters. In any case, there was still a fair amount of room and there was a general shifting around of all the tribes in the area until the arrival of the Europeans.

The pastoralist conquerors did one of three things. Perhaps, like the Masai, having found the land they wanted, they settled on it, pushing elsewhere whoever was there before them. And having settled on it, they ignored the cultivators around them. They looked down on the farmers because they had no cattle, and the pastoralists thought of them as not being men. They wanted to have as little contact with them as possible, and they maintained as complete a separation as they could. The feeling was mutual, and the cultivators were just as glad to have nothing to do with the pastoralists, and so long as neither tried to take land from the other there was no conflict. Other pastoralists who were particularly successful as fighters established control over the people they conquered. They kept their own pastoral way of life, but they exacted tribute from the cultivators they had conquered, and they ruled over them. As the rulers they formed a sort of pastoral aristocracy on their own, and again did not have to mix with the lower class of cultivators. Such were the Watusi, the seven-foot giants of Ruanda Urundi.

A third way of dealing with the situation was adopted in areas where perhaps the pastoral peoples did not have sufficient cattle left to live on, or were neither numerous nor powerful enough and were forced to be more dependent on the cultivators whose land they had entered. Whereas other pastoralists, like the Masai, believe that their god gave them cattle and that it is as wrong for others to possess cattle as it is for them to cultivate, these people practiced the policy of assimilation. They adopted cultivation, and the cultivators adopted cattle. Among these people, mostly in the lake region, it is now nearly impossible to tell the earlier inhabitants from the later. But cattle still give prestige and form an important part of ritual life.

So strongly was ritual life tied in with the cattle that those pastoralists who pushed right down into the tsetse belt have retained many customs connected with cattle even though they have lost all their cattle and have for generations lived entirely by cultivation. There is, then, throughout the Nile Valley, East Africa, and southern Africa, a vast number of people who traditionally are pastoralists rather than cultivators and to whom cattle represent more than a mere source of food and clothing. To them cattle represent wealth and status. But even more important, cattle—even if they are only few in number—remind these people of the ways of their fathers and of their beliefs. In the same way that the Pygmy hunters make the forest the center of their life, relating everything to it, saying that something is good because it is good for the forest, so these pastoral peoples make cattle the center of their life. The cow and the ox stand as a symbol of their unity in this world and the next, a symbol of the law-abiding life that they are expected to lead. Although the old beliefs die hard, once their cattle are taken away from them, the old way of life begins to crumble.

These people never achieved the kind of civilization that the ancient Egyptians did, but we have seen some of the reasons. Much more important, however, they did achieve many of those qualities that we generally think of as belonging only to what we call civilization. They respect their families, they respect the cattle that give them life, they respect life itself. If there is little elaborate political organization, it is generally because there is no need for it. Unless they were under pressure from other tribes they were able to remain in relatively small self-governing groups. But when there was outside pressure they proved themselves equal, refusing to be conquered, always either conquering or simply moving elsewhere.

But theirs is a tradition, because it is so nomadic and demands so much of men and women alike, that does not fit easily into the modern world. Some pastoral peoples have made the adaptation to an economy that includes farming, and for them the problem is less acute. But for those who maintain the old way without change, there is little hope. The need for land is great, and there is not space enough for huge herds of cattle to roam at will. And as the cattle die off, so will the people.

THE CULTIVATORS

We have seen how neither hunting nor pastoralism really makes for a natural growth of what we call civilization. Law and order are maintained in the small, relatively isolated groups in which these people live, partly by the authority of the senior member of the family, partly because of the necessity for close cooperation, and partly by a belief that their particular way of life was given to their ancestors by God and that to depart from it would be to invite disaster. To the Pygmies the forest is as sacred as are cattle to the pastoralists, and this ritual belief forms a solid core around which the isolated groups can all unite in times of crisis.

We saw how particularly amongst the pastoralists there was need to unite every now and again both for defense and offense, and how, through the age-set system, bonds are formed between men of the same age regardless of their more local family loyalties. The system of grouping peoples by their age also corresponds to certain economic and political needs. Children generally help their mothers, and boys can be made to do the work of women. But once a boy is initiated and becomes a man, he becomes the protector of his people, the protector of cattle. This is his full-time job, and much of his life at this stage is spent apart from the others. The entry of a boy into adulthood is the signal for his father to pass into the third stage—that of the elders. He may not do so at once, but soon he will have to become an elder, leaving the work of protection to his sons. As an elder he has another job, that of making decisions affecting the group as a whole and of settling disputes. A number of senior elders together may form a council, but there is virtually no form of chieftainship.

If there is any very great crisis, then there are ritual specialists, priests who have special powers and who, because they are a class apart, do not have strong family loyalties which might make them biased on one side as against the other. But even their authority, such as it is, is not backed by any material power.

There is no police force. The priests have authority only because they represent the belief of the people; this belief is the real power. It is a simple system of organization, but it is completely effective for the pastoral kind of life. Its apparent informality made things difficult for the colonial administrators who wanted some central authority, such as a chief, to deal with; so much so that in some cases they actually insisted on appointing chiefs.

Generally, cultivators have more complex systems, but not necessarily. The Kikuyu of Kenya, like the pastoralists, had no chiefs, but lived an extremely ordered life under the authority only of councils of elders. The Kikuyu are among those tribes on whom the British administration forced chieftainship, though it was totally foreign to them, and from whom they alienated traditional lands. And when foreign elements like this are forcibly introduced, no matter how good the reason, a whole series of repercussions are set in motion, like a chain reaction. The end result, in this case, was Mau Mau, a blind and bitter uprising against colonialism.

Before we look at some of the cultivators who have evolved highly complex organizations developing into kingdoms and empires, let us look more closely at the Kikuyu. Here again we see how local geography plays an important part. The Kikuyu got their land from an earlier group of inhabitants who were hunters, the Ndorobo. It is in the Kenya highlands, a wooded terrain of steeply sloping ridges interlaced with streams. Of course the ridges are not nearly so far apart nor so isolated as are the hilltops of the pastoral Nuer, but they do form natural divisions, and each one in a sense is independent. The Kikuyu have three names that apply to these ridges, which gives us some idea of how closely the land is linked to the life of the people.

The ridge itself is called *rogongo,* that is, the geographical unit of high land divided from others by valleys and streams. Then the land on the ridge, particularly the land which is cultivated, is called *githaka.* And the extended family who live on the *rogongo* and cultivate the *githaka,* form what is known as *mbari.*

An *mbari* consists of a number of homesteads, each with a large round house with mud walls and thatch roof, about thirty-five feet in diameter. Each house has its own courtyard and a place for a few cattle, some sheep, goats, and poultry. There is one such homestead for each adult member of the family, young girls sleeping in the same house as their mother, boys often sleeping in special bachelor houses. For all the homesteads form-ing an *mbari* there is the *githaka,* the plot of land that is farmed by each woman separately in her own section, but for the com-mon good. Each *mbari* is a tightly knit family and economic organization. It is largely self-supporting, and unlike the case of the pastoralists, there is no need for constant moving about in search for fresh land. Only when an *mbari* becomes too crowded does the family split, one member going off on his own to found another settlement.

A Kikuyu man may have several wives, and for each wife there will be a special homestead for her and her children, and a spe-cial section of the common *githaka* for her to farm. But an *mbari* consists of more than just a single family. There are a number of related families. A man's sons will live with him; and their sons and their sons' sons will all live together for as long as there is sufficient land. To the cultivators the soil is sacred, and the right to use it is the most cherished possession that a man passes on to his children. Each child inherits the right to the use of the soil cultivated by his mother, and an *mbari* always provides a mother with enough land to support her family. So the size of an *mbari,* although sometimes as small as thirty or forty men, women, and children, may rise to several thousand. Usually, however, it seems to be around four or five hundred.

One of the major occasions for meeting people of another ridge, another *mbari,* is the occasion of marriage. When a girl marries she always leaves her own home and joins her husband's *mbari.* Otherwise there is not much interchange. So, much like the pastoralists, the Kikuyu have an age-set system where all boys who are initiated in the same year, regardless of what *mbari* they belong to, consider themselves as brothers. Members of the same age set are bound to offer help and protection to each other whenever it is demanded, and as with the pastoralists this gives the Kikuyu a wider sense of unity than they would other-wise have. It also forms the basis for an all-embracing social organization. Six distinct stages of life are recognized, each with its own duties and responsibilities, and the age sets pass, one by one, through each of these stages. The unity this system gives to the Kikuyu is reinforced by their strong attachment to the land they cultivate.

We have already said that the system of inheritance is for a boy to inherit the right to farm the land that was farmed by his mother. He does not inherit the land itself, he can not dispose of it, and he can not fix any clear boundaries. What he is entitled to is the fruit of a portion of the land that belongs to his people as a whole. So although he does not inherit a clearly defined plot of land which he can sell or exchange at will, it does mean that simply by being a Kikuyu he has a permanent right to farm his share.

The troubles that led to Mau Mau began when the early European settlers found what they thought was a lot of unused land, and wanted to purchase it for their own use. They offered money to the Kikuyu, who accepted it; but each side had a different idea as to the exact nature of the transaction. The European thought that he had bought the land outright, the soil and the fruit it bore, and the minerals it contained. He thought it was his to do with whatever he liked, to sell again to someone else if he wanted. But to the Kikuyu all that had happened was that he had agreed to let the European farm the land and take the fruit of his labor. For even if all the leaders of all the *mbari* of the Kikuyu got together, they would not have the right to sell a single acre.

Their belief is that the land belongs to the tribe, and that means not only the living, but the dead and the unborn. The dead are buried on the land, so how can one sell their bones? Those who are to be born will be born with the same rights as every living Kikuyu, and in particular the right to farm his share of the land. To sell the land, then, would be to sell the birthright of future generations. Neither side understood the other, and as the Europeans quickly bought up all the best farming land in the country this brought about a serious economic, political, and religious crisis, leading directly to the Kikuyu rebellion.

Sometimes the African cultivators are even less centrally organized than the Kikuyu, who did at least have councils of elders drawn from the various *mbari*. For instance, those cultivators who were forced from the plains of East Africa into the dense tropical forest necessarily had to split up into small isolated communities. To farm they had to cut down the trees and burn the stumps to prepare the land for planting and allow enough sunlight to reach the soil. They settled in these clearings in small, tightly packed villages, built so that they could be easily defended. Each village was separated from the next by many miles of a forest that was, to the villagers, highly dangerous.

So each village was an independent unit under the leadership of a headman. This headman was usually the descendant of the first man who founded the village, the first man to begin cutting the trees and burning the land. And life in these villages was simple to the extreme. The men did all the hard work of cutting and clearing, and the women planted and tended the crops. At all times the men had to stand by in case of attack, either by enemy tribes or by animals. Once the tribal movements came to a halt and the warfare ceased, the men were no longer needed for fighting, but they were still needed as guards.

It is by no means true that men in Africa let women do all the work. Generally labor is divided fairly, with everyone—including the children—doing their share. Women certainly do more physical work than most European or American women, but they are proud of their physical strength and of their responsibility, and would not have it otherwise. The men do any really heavy work, such as clearing the forest for planting, but their main work is protection. They do the dangerous work too, such as hunting (though there are many forest cultivators who do not hunt other than by digging traps around the plantation) and fishing among the fast flowing rapids of the forest rivers.

After a cooked meal early in the morning, men and women go about their work, returning to the village in the late afternoon when the main meal is eaten. In the forest area this will be manioc—a starchy root that can be roasted, fried, or ground to a flour and made into stodgy bread—or banana. Sometimes dry rice is grown in the plantations, and nearly every woman has a small plot for peanuts and corn, and perhaps some beans. The men may be able to add meat or fish to the diet, making it more sufficient and varied, or they may rely on neighboring hunters for meat. There is little time for relaxation. In a sense these people are nomadic, too, as every three years or so the soil becomes exhausted and they have to move on, laboriously cutting another plantation out of the virgin forest.

Thus, the forest cultivators do not become very attached to the land they live on; rather do they think of the forest as being an unfriendly place because it makes life so hard for them. The soil refuses to support their meager crops for more than three years, yet it gives life in abundance to the huge, towering forest trees. But at least there is rain all year round, and the cultivators here do not have to worry about drought.

Their fears are more fears of the forest: fear that the soil will suddenly refuse to bear their crops; fear that the animals of the forest—particularly baboons or elephants—will raid the plantation and destroy it; fear that the leopard will enter the village at night and steal the few scrawny goats or chickens they manage to raise; fear that the vicious forest buffalo will attack the women and children when they go down to the stream to get water or to bathe, or when they go into the forest to gather firewood.

There are other dangers too. Most of the forest trees grow to around a hundred and fifty feet in height, and they are as big as a house at the base. Every now and again, when the roots grow old and infirm, or when the tree dies, these giants come crashing down, bringing smaller trees with them. It can happen quite suddenly, bringing death and destruction. For this reason the villagers often cut a circle around their village and even around the plantation, about two hundred feet back from the edge, so that they will be safe. It may take a whole day to cut a single tree, sometimes longer, so it is no wonder that the villagers do not have kindly feelings toward the forest. On the contrary, they people it with evil spirits, regarding it as the source of all their misfortune.

Many of the tribes in this area, being somewhat isolated and split up into independent villages, are organized around the family system: large families formed into clans. Each clan has its totem, some kind of animal that they respect. They regard it as the embodiment of one of the forest spirits. By respecting it, not killing it or harming it or eating its flesh even if killed by someone else, they hope to secure its help and protection. Sometimes they will invent a myth to explain why they have chosen a particular animal. They will say that a crocodile, for instance, helped their ancestor when he first entered the forest, cut down the trees, and burned the land to make the first plantation. Perhaps the crocodile saved the ancestor's life by biting the leg of a buffalo that was about to attack him. And for such a reason all the descendants of that ancestor are bound to respect the life of the crocodile. This is, incidentally, often a good way of knowing if someone is related to you, since anyone from your tribe who respects the crocodile is descended from the same ancestor and so belongs to the same clan.

But it is when we get to the cultivators of the open grasslands, rather than those who live in the mountains or the forest, that we find a major development taking place. For in the open country there are not the same natural barriers dividing one settlement from another. The family grows naturally into a clan, a series of clans into a tribe, and sometimes a series of tribes into a nation, or even an empire. The cultivators who pushed right through the forest from the northwest established such kingdoms and empires when they reached its southern edge. There they were free to expand as those in the dense forest were not.

At one time the empires of the Kongo and the Kuba, the Luba and the Lunda, stretched almost from coast to coast, and they were responsible for the enormous growth in the economic and political systems of the various tribes. They were also responsible for a tremendous development in the arts and crafts, particularly music and sculpture. For when you have a kingdom, with a king surrounded by his court, you get both the time and the incentive to develop such luxuries. In much the same way as the princes of medieval Europe, the African kings were patrons of the arts. They had amassed sufficient wealth by conquest and through the exacting of tribute to be able to afford to provide artists with food in return for their work. The artists were given special privileges and protection. As a result you find some magnificent carving in ivory and wood (two of the commonest materials in this area) and fine metalwork in bronze, gold, and iron dating back as far as the sixteenth century.

In a sense this work is better called craft than art, because nearly all wood carvings and metal castings were functional, utilitarian. Stools, for instance, were sometimes elaborately decorated with animal and human forms, but this was not done for artistic effect. It was rather to indicate the status of the owner or to reinforce tribal values. Motherhood is often depicted in African sculpture because childbearing is considered a blessing not only to the individual family, but to the whole tribe as well. The features are often distorted to give special emphasis; a head is enlarged to convey the idea of wisdom, the trunk and arms made heavier to give an impression of strength. Sometimes a personal or clan totem is represented in carved household furniture to serve as a constant reminder of the ever watchful presence of ancestral spirits.

Even music is functional, being used to accompany dances that are often ritual and symbolic, but also, and perhaps mainly, music is used for communication. Drums and wooden slit-gongs are beaten in rhythmic and melodic patterns that can be translated into words; the "talking drum" of West Africa actually imitates the sound and tonal pattern of the spoken language. And music is also used, as we saw with the Bushmen and Pygmies, to communicate with the world beyond.

Of course, there is also elaboration in other aspects of life. You tend to get individual families owning their land and farming it for their own benefit, paying a certain amount of tribute or tax to the local headman or chief. These local headmen may, in fact, be senior members of the local clan, and they may elect chiefs; or again the chief may simply be the most senior member of the larger family.

But generally there is some system of delegated authority all the way up from the individual family, through headmen and chiefs, to the king. The individual no longer has to worry about his personal protection; that is taken care of by his superiors to whom he pays tribute. He may be able to specialize in some way, growing a certain kind of crop only, or living as a craftsman, making agricultural tools or household furniture; for this kind of society provides for a growth of trade and for the beginnings of markets. Instead of each family providing for its own needs, making its own clothes as well as its own furniture and supplying its own food, this self-sufficiency is replaced by specialization of labor. Many of these states developed monetary systems, though the usual practice was, and in tribal areas still is, a simple exchange of one kind of goods for another.

Amongst nearly all cultivators the market has come to be a major factor in their lives. It is not only where they exchange goods, often carried for miles balanced in tall tiers on the heads of the women, but it is also where they meet friends and relatives and discuss local affairs. The women tend to form one group, the men another, and members of each group air their grievances in public and expect the others to make comment. Sometimes minor disputes are settled effectively in this simple way, public discussion and the voice of common opinion being considered as sufficient. Often the culprit is ridiculed in public, and this is as sure a means of preventing any further misbehavior on his part as any. Sometimes the local chief or headman will hold his tribunal to settle major disputes on market day so that everyone will have the chance to take part.

Even in the great kingdoms disputes were generally settled at the lowest possible level, the idea being rather to restore harmony than to inflict punishment, but the threat of physical retribution was there.

If a dispute arose, it was brought to the headman. If he could not settle it, it went to the chief, and from him to the king. And now there was a body of specialists whose job it was to enforce the law. Man was becoming civilized and his world too complex for him to live an ordered life without any threat of coercion simply because he believed in that way. Now he lived as he did because he was afraid of the punishment that would follow if he did not.

Even religion was becoming less and less of a personal matter. In the same way that there was economic and political specialization, so was there also ritual specialization. There was a whole new caste of witch doctors and priests who alone could perform the necessary rites, for which they had to be paid. It

was a far cry from the Bushmen, who simply sang to the sky, or the Pygmies, who sang to the forest in times of crisis or need.

But this was all part of the system of delegation of authority and responsibility. A kingdom could not afford to have a number of families or villages each being a law to itself, each independent of the other. And yet it did not need to be despotic. To start with, it grew inevitably out of a situation in which perhaps the discovery of agriculture and animal husbandry resulted in a sudden increase in the population. It also resulted in communities not only being larger, but much more settled. An argument could no longer be settled simply by leaving it to the next day, or by expecting one family or the other to move elsewhere. There was none of the earlier need for mutual cooperation, so in the case of a dispute neither side was willing to give way, and it had to be settled from outside. And with an ever-growing community there was much more need for a strong central authority that was not bound by family ties.

In this kind of agricultural community, which comprised

members of many different families, and even total strangers, a representative of the original founder would no longer be any good. He would be bound to be prejudiced in favor of his own family. So if a leader was chosen because of his ancestry, a number of checks were put on his power. The witch doctor or priest was one such check, balancing secular authority with sacred, the force of arms with the force of the supernatural.

Even in the apparently most despotic traditional states in Africa we should be aware of this, and if we look more closely we often find that, in fact, these states were essentially democratic. The king was regarded as the head of the tribe just as a father is the head of a family; he represented his "family," he ruled, in most cases, by their consent, and he fulfilled their wishes. His own future depended on theirs, and they in turn believed that their future depended on his. In some instances he had little individual power; in others his power was enormous. But always there were checks and controls on that power, and the people themselves were the ultimate control.

The BaGanda of eastern Africa, for instance, have a king who can trace his ancestry back over a thousand years. At the time of the British occupation barely half a century ago the king, or Kabaka, was apparently all powerful. There were stories about how at his accession to the throne thousands of people were slaughtered or buried alive, and of how he held the power of life and death. Now it is true that there were some ritual sacrifices at the accession of a new Kabaka, but they were considered necessary for the safety and welfare of the nation, and many of them were voluntary. People offered their lives believing that they would win favor in the afterworld in this way, and sacrificial ritual could never have been carried out had there not been an acceptance at all levels of the belief that it was necessary.

The BaGanda are cultivators who early adopted pastoralism as well. Their land is lush and plentiful, and they attributed all their good fortune. to the ancestor of the Kabaka, who first settled the land. The coronation ritual was, in fact, a perfect re-enactment of the original act of settlement, even to the killings. It was believed that so long as the re-enactment was faithful, the same success and prosperity that followed the original accession would follow all others. People who died, did so in order that the nation as a whole might live, and there were many who actually volunteered to die in the belief that in so doing they would earn for themselves a favorite position in the world of the ancestors. And to be born of royal line was not exactly a blessing, for when a Kabaka died, all his sons were summoned together. The council of advisers to the dead king then elected his successor from amongst the sons. They chose the son they thought would make the wisest ruler. The others were exiled, as they knew they would be. If this were not done, there would probably have been endless fighting amongst them, each one claiming that he should have been elected Kabaka.

In some African kingdoms the king was only allowed to reign for a short time, and he was then ritually killed. He knew this when he was elected; he was willing to make the sacrifice because he believed it would not only bring him reward in the afterlife, but that it was necessary to ensure the continued prosperity of his people. When a king died, there were many who would volunteer to be killed and buried with him so that they could provide him with a fitting attendance when he entered the afterworld.

In fact, it was relatively seldom that a king in Africa, or even a chief, was the sole undisputed power. More often than not he really had no practical power, but was more a symbol of the unity of his people and a link between them in this world and their ancestors in the world beyond. Certain rituals were entirely in the king's hands. In some cases he was responsible for the rain, for the fertility of the fields, for the successful harvesting of the crops—for these were the chief concern of the grassland cultivators. Unlike the cultivators of the forest, they could not count on the rain's coming when it was wanted, and they were constantly in danger of losing their entire crop either because of too little rain or too much.

Sometimes also the king acted as the final court of appeal, but generally his function was symbolic or ritual. What power he had was checked by a council, and often there was yet another power—the queen mother. She might be the king's mother or an older sister, but the important thing was that she represented another family, and this avoided any charges of partiality that might otherwise have been leveled against the king. The Kabaka of BuGanda,* in fact, was customarily married to many wives, all from different commoner families, to emphasize that he took no sides.

But it is on the west coast of Africa that some of the most complex states have evolved. We do not have time to look at them all, but it is worth noting that they all had their roots in simpler cultivating societies, and came to be the great nations they are by the inevitable and natural sequence of events that is bound to follow the adoption of a settled economy. One of the greatest of these states is the Ashanti, one of the major groups in the present nation of Ghana. Ghana itself is the name of an African nation dating back to somewhere around the thirteenth century.

It was about this time that the Akan peoples began coming

* Bantu languages are characterized by the use of prefixes. So, a MuGanda lives in BuGanda, and talks LuGanda to all the other BaGanda. C.T..

down from the western Sudan into the north of what is now
Ghana. Their present-day descendants are much darker than
the Bantu of eastern and southern Africa, and there being less
mixture, they have a purer Negroid appearance. They are also
considerably shorter than the tall Sudanic and Nilotic tribes.
They were already organized into families, lineages, clans and
tribes, and they were industrious cultivators. They practiced a
system of tracing descent that is common in Africa, but very
different from ours.

Instead of tracing descent through the father, taking the
father's name and inheriting the father's property, a child
traced his descent through his mother's line, and at an early age
a boy went to live with his mother's brother, from whom he
would inherit—not from his father. It was mainly land that was
inherited, and the land was of particular significance not only
because it provided the means of livelihood but also because it
was thought to be the resting place of the spirits of the dead.

The position of women was in many ways higher than that of
men, for they worked the fields, and they were considered as
being responsible for the fertility of the fields through the fertility of their own bodies. They gave life to children, so also did
they have power to give life to the crops in the soil. In the
family then, it was the mother who ruled, for it was her land
and her wealth on which they lived. But in effect the division of
labor was much the same, with the man doing the really heavy
work, and seeing to the protection of his family, while the
woman hoed the fields.

So that although inheritance was traced through the mother,
a balance of power was found in giving an additional role to
the father. The mother was thought of as actually passing on
"blood" or *mogya,* when she gave birth to a child. There could

be no doubts about the identity of the mother, the child being "born from her stomach," but there was no sure way of proving who the father was. So the mother passed on the "blood," and the father, who otherwise would have had no status at all in the family, passed on something called *ntoro,* a kind of spiritual substance which had to be inherited just as much as "blood," but which had more relevance to the afterlife than to the present.

The mother, then, was the practical head of the household, particularly in any matters concerning food or the land; the father was the spiritual head. Also, partly because of his physical superiority, he was made the political head—but not of his own immediate family, rather of the family of his mother and his sisters. It sounds complicated, but that is because we think of the family as comprising a father and mother and their children.

To the Ashanti, however, and to the many African farmers who practice matrilineal descent, as it is called, the "family" (*abusua*) consists of a brother, his sister, and her children. A man's land and possessions are inherited by his nephew, specifically by his sister's son, not by another brother's son. This is the case because, tracing descent through the female line, his sister's son will have the same *mogya,* or "blood," as he does; where say his brother's son, or his own, will have different *mogya*—that of their own mothers. To his own son a father passes on only *ntoro,* or "spirit."

When families—in this new sense—group together then, the leader is a man, but the actual family head is his sister. While he may be given the job of administering justice, his sister is the real power and she will reserve for herself all matters pertaining to women. And as the Akan peoples settled in their new homeland many hundreds of years ago and they found that they needed to band together more closely because of hostile tribes around them, the same system prevailed. The men, naturally, were the fighters and organized all matters concerning defense or offensive warfare. But they never assumed complete control. Even when families formed into clans and tribes, each with its chief, the chief was always succeeded by a sister's son, never by his own son. And whenever a chief sat in judgment, his sister was there behind him to give him advice and to make up his mind for him if he was in doubt or in danger of giving a wrong decision.

There was a whole mythology associated with this system whereby, some say, the queen mother represented the moon goddess, and the king, her brother, represented the sun god. The moon and the sun and five other planets were represented by the division of a clan into seven lineages, and of a tribe into seven clans. At the head of each unit—be it family, lineage, clan, or tribe—the pattern was to have a male leader, directly influenced and checked by his sister or mother. When the seven Akan tribes met to consider how they could best unite against their enemies, the same pattern was followed and the Ashanti Confederacy was formed, uniting the seven tribes under a single queen mother and king.

This constant division and subdivision of the group along these lines meant that no one leader, either of a family or of the Confederacy, had anything like absolute power. And as if to emphasize that the existing power was divine and not mortal, the symbol of authority throughout the Akan peoples was the Stool. There were stools for men and stools for women, and they were thought to contain the soul of the people. They were the real power; they were far more sacred than the person of the king. At the time of the meeting of the seven Akan tribes the major problem was how to decide which of their chiefs should

become the "paramount chief." The chief of the Kumasi tribe must have had a particularly clever ritual adviser, for he proposed that they should all sit around in a circle and invoke the symbol of their unity—a stool that would contain the soul of the entire nation. This would come from the skies, and it would alight on the knees of whoever was to be the paramount chief. All agreed, and after the necessary invocations, there was a rolling of thunder; and out of the stormy sky came a golden stool, slowly alighting on the knees of the chief of the Kumasi tribe, who was promptly proclaimed Ashantihene, or King of the Ashanti. But the Ashantihene has never sat on the Golden Stool, for that would have been a desecration. It is always placed beside him, raised from the ground, as the symbol of the unity of the entire nation.

Another example of misunderstanding, and its disastrous consequences, is that of a junior British officer who was sent to sign
a peace treaty with the Ashantihene in the nineteenth century,
when the British were fighting to extend their authority farther
inland. The officer demanded that the Golden Stool be brought
for him to sit on. He thought that it was merely a kind of throne,
and that as the queen's representative it was his right to sit on
it. This was taken by the Ashanti as a direct insult, and even
worse his subsequent attempts to capture the Stool by force were
taken as a blatant admission of the intention of the British to
enslave the soul of the Ashanti people. The last of the bloody
Ashanti wars resulted, and still more serious, there began a long
period of mistrust between the two peoples. But although the
Ashantihene was exiled, the Golden Stool was concealed and

never captured, and the Ashanti people were never truly defeated—their soul remained intact. When the Ashantihene returned from exile, the Stool was once more brought out, and is still used as the symbol of Ashanti unity.

The Ashanti were not only farmers, they were also traders. The land yielded gold, making possible an elaborate monetary system, and there were a number of large commercial centers. With a population of almost a million, all united into a military confederacy, a complex form of social control was called for.

Once again the ritual belief of the individual was no longer enough; he could not be left to his own ways, acting primarily in the interests of his family. There had to be some form of authority imposed from without. But as has already been seen, the authority of the Ashantihene was balanced more than evenly by that of the queen mother, and he was surrounded by an elaborate court who kept a watchful eye on him and effectively prevented any abuse of his personal power. He stood at the head of the state as a symbol of the soul of the nation, as a symbol of impartiality.

The laws that were devised over the years may seem strange today, and some of the punishments that were inflicted may seem brutal, but they were all imposed through this central figure, and therefore with the strict impartiality of common consent and for the common good. And further, though the punishments may seem brutal—sometimes involving maiming or mutilation of the body—they were no more brutal than many of the punishments in practice in Europe at the same time. And more important still, if we are to understand the system and not just look at it as an example of "primitive savagery," the laws were widely known, and so were the punishments for breaking them. Anyone who committed a crime knew exactly what the penalty was, and so had no legitimate complaint.

The laws were designed to protect the system, to ensure the correct inheritance of the land, keeping it within the *abusua* at all times, for to do otherwise would be a desecration, inviting disaster upon the whole tribe. The law also enforced an unfailing respect for the Ashantihene, the greatest crime of all being to utter an oath bringing the Ashantihene into disrepute.

The African tradition is not one of tribal warfare, of bloodshed, of magic and sorcery, of ruthless despots. It is a tradition of a constant attempt to stabilize a rapidly changing society by the most effective means possible. Where there was no need for war, there was no war, and every device was used to divert hostilities in other directions—by ridicule, threat of exile, or whatever—so as to avoid the bloodshed that might lead to war.

Leadership is generally on a family basis, the concept of the family actually varying and expanding to considerable degrees throughout the continent. Only when there are large settled populations (as occurs only with cultivators), does one find the complex machinery of a central government, and even then it follows the traditional family pattern, with the myth that the head of the state is essentially the father, representing the original ancestor, or the founder of the tribe. Any action that is taken within that tribe in the name of the chief or king is taken not for his personal gain, but for the common good of the "family" as a whole.

There have been exceptions, dictators and tyrants, as there are in every society. But generally they have met with an early and fitting end. For this also is the African tradition: The office a man holds, representing his people and their forefathers, is more sacred than the man.

THE WAY OF THE ANCESTORS

The greatest obstacle to overcome in understanding the peoples of Africa is the constant appearance of customs and concepts that are so very different from our own. When we look at them in their own context, however, they seem less strange. Of all these customs, those concerning a belief in the supernatural are probably the hardest to grasp: Magic, witchcraft, and sorcery are concepts totally concealed in everyday life in the western world. But belief in the afterlife and in the critical presence of ancestral spirits is a major theme in most African societies. Although it is dangerous to generalize, we have to try and see the basic ways in which these beliefs affect everyday life in Africa.

What we have been trying to do is to understand what makes the different kinds of society and tradition what they are, and what keeps them that way; what it is that maintains the law and order that is so characteristic of tribal life for all its apparent informality and lack of professional police and politicians. We have seen throughout that the family, and the respect felt by each member of the family for every other member, is one such force toward order. We have seen how this feeling of kinship is

92

so strong that the family has been taken as the model for the organization of the clans, even of tribes and nations. And we have also seen how, in order to avoid the danger of one-sided loyalties, age sets are made to cut across family bonds, uniting all members of a given community, using common age rather than common kinship as the deciding factor.

But all this is not enough. Almost everywhere the respect felt for the family extends beyond the family of the living; it extends both forward and backward in time. We saw this clearly with the Kikuyu, for whom it is impossible to part with land because it belongs to the family in its widest sense—the living and the dead, and the unborn yet to come.

While there are no single generalizations that we can make about ancestor worship in Africa, it is plain that given this concept of the family, there must be considerable respect for ancestors. But in every region, even among neighboring tribes, more detailed attitudes vary widely. For instance, both of the major groups of hunters, the desert Bushmen and the forest Pygmies, only have a very vague and hazy notion of who their ancestors were. They do not trace their families back for endless generations and then arrive at a name and say, "He was the ancestor of us all." Most of them can barely remember the names of their grandfathers and what families they came from, and it is rare indeed that anyone knows the name of his great-grandfather.

But these people live in very close family groups. They are not formed strictly on either the mother's or father's side, and there are no very rigid rules, as there are elsewhere, about residence. A hunter can go off to live with his wife's group if he wants to, but more often she will come to live with him because by the time he is married he will already have formed a number of close friendships with those people with whom he likes to hunt, and this always makes for a safer and better hunt. But even though any single hunting band is made up of several different families, they all think of themselves as one, and they acknowledge their common bond in that they *are* hunters, depending on each other, and all depending on the forest.

They generally only mention the past when there is some dissension, and then they quote what their fathers and mothers used to say and do. There is a definite belief that the old ways are best, and if anything goes wrong, it is frequently blamed on the introduction of some innovation. And there are certain things that the hunters do, the exact meaning of which they have forgotten themselves, but which they still do because they were taught to do it by their fathers. Some of the words they use in their sacred songs have quite lost their meaning, but they are carefully preserved and passed on from one generation to another, never changing, because they are the songs of the ancestors, and therefore old, and therefore good.

With the hunters it is not that the ancestors themselves are sacred. It is rather that the living believe that in the very olden times things were even better than they are now, and that the hunters of those days were closer to the spirits and gods than are the hunters of today. They would like to recapture those old days, and they think that by imitating the ways of their fathers as nearly as possible they will be better off than by trying new ways. In fact, with the hunters the tendency is to by-pass the ancestors and deal more directly with the spiritual world. To do this they have to use the knowledge their fathers passed on to them, but that is all. They sing their sacred songs, they dance their sacred dances, not with the ancestors in mind but thinking rather of the unseen power that somehow controls their lives.

There is only one such power, they believe, and so in a way they all only worship one god. For the Bushmen and for the Pygmies alike, this god is vaguely defined, but in both cases he has something to do with the natural world all around them.

For the Pygmies it is the forest itself—the greatest source of their unity, the greatest source of strength, and the greatest incentive to live peaceful, ordered lives. They are not even particularly concerned about life in the world beyond. That is too far away for them even to think about it. How can they know what it is like, they ask, when they have never been there? They are concerned mainly with living their life in this world the best way possible, and letting the next world take care of itself. And to live life well here it has to be pleasing to their fathers, and above all it has to be pleasing to the forest. This is what binds the hunters together, with bonds tighter than could be forged by any system of central government or by any system of enforced law. They behave as they behave not because they have to, but because they want to, because they believe that it is the best way and therefore the right way.

With the pastoralists we get a different emphasis, but basically the belief is the same as with the hunters. Cattle to the pastoralists, are what the forest is to the Pygmies. Cattle are the suppliers of life, the source of all welfare and honor. Consideration for cattle forms the center of pastoral life. People like the Masai believe that cattle were given to them by their god, and this is a source of great pride. At the same time it gives them the responsibility for caring for this gift, in this way deserving continued blessing.

There are some who say that the Masai do not believe in an afterlife, but the Masai sometimes use the names of the dead when they invoke aid in times of crisis, and they have other customs that indicate that although they give an afterlife no great thought, this does not mean actual disbelief. To be sure, they put the bodies of their dead out in the open for the hyenas to dispose of them—rather than pollute the pasture land with rotting corpses by burying them. But when they do this they place the body in a special posture, with new sandals and a stick for its journey beyond, and some grass placed in one hand in the traditional greeting of peace. This certainly indicates some belief in the world beyond.

Perhaps their position is much like that of the hunters. They have not been to the afterworld, so they do not know what it is like and are not going to waste time speculating about it. They are more concerned with living out their life in the way they have been taught. And here, also like the hunters, they believe that the old ways are the good ways, and any departure is thought to bring misfortune not only to the individual but to the whole group. For a man is not alone; he represents his family, and whatever he does he does in the name they share with him. In this way a man can be made to feel responsible for the entire tribe.

With some of the other pastoralists there is a more conscious belief in an afterlife and in the spirits that govern life in this world, sometimes helping and sometimes making mischief. The ancestors can be invoked for their aid in time of crisis, in the belief that they will intercede between their children and the spirits of the afterworld. The supernatural can not be approached directly, as it can by the hunters, but only through the intercession of the ancestors. This is a good reason for respecting the ancestors, and for occasionally propitiating them, remembering their names, making sacrifices to them, and so on. Cattle are still of prime importance, and are involved in any sacrifice or ceremonial feast. But the belief is becoming more complex.

You also get among some of these pastoralists the beginnings of totemic worship, together with ancestor worship, this being a way of dividing the tribe clearly into large family groups. The totems, generally animals, stand as symbols of the various subdivisions and are frequently connected in some way, in the mythology, with the ancestors. But generally the people are still essentially practical, and their initiations are into age sets that have very practical functions, particularly connected with the care of cattle and the protection of the tribe rather than anything else. It is with the cultivators that initiation is more directly connected with ancestor worship.

With the hunters and gatherers, initiation into adulthood was little more than proof by a boy that he was able to do the work of a man—that is, kill a large antelope or a similar animal, so providing food for a family. This entitled him to consider himself as an adult, ready to contemplate marriage, and in the case of the Pygmies it also entitled him to sing the sacred songs of the *molimo,* the greatest of all religious festivals, and to communicate directly through the songs with the god of the forest.

Whereas for both the pastoralists and the hunters, initiation of boys into adulthood affects their economic status, initiation of boys among the cultivators is concerned more with their religious life. Here, initiation often takes the form of a period at puberty in which the boys have to undergo a series of ordeals, toughening them up physically and mentally. They also have to undergo a whole series of rites that purify them, sometimes being ritually "killed" as children, and "reborn" as men. They become new and different people. They also learn, during this period, all the secrets of tribal lore, so that they become men with sacred knowledge. And it is only through initiation that they can prove that they are fit to serve the ancestors in this life and join them in the afterlife.

Boys who are not initiated are considered children; they have no chance to learn the tribal lore, and so they can not perform any of the sacred rights. The belief is that they are unclean and will not be able to join the ancestors. They are social outcasts in this life and the next. For the cultivators, this initiation is one of the most important events in their lives. And also among the cultivators, since the woman is so important through her work in the fields, there are various forms of initiation that cleanse the girls at the time of puberty, making them fit for the life that lies ahead. And by "fit" is generally meant "pleasing to the ancestors."

It is really quite reasonable, so long as we keep in mind the African notion of the tribe as including the living, the dead, and the unborn. The ancestors are those of the tribe who are now living elsewhere, and life has to be lived in a way that will be pleasing to them by those whom they have left here as their representatives. The pleasing way is the old way, the way the ancestors used to live.

But they are also pleased by other things: If the tribe of the living grows large and powerful, they are pleased; if its men are courageous and its women bear many children, they are pleased. Sometimes it is believed that the ancestors like to revisit the land of the living, so they have to be provided with places to stay. Thus, Spirit Houses are built for them, and offerings of food are made to show they are welcome and constantly thought of. Sometimes a wooden figure is carved, representing a human being or maybe the totemic animal, and it is thought that the spirit settles there. Sometimes it can be invoked by special prayer or sacrifice, to come to the help of the living in times of need. In fact, the ancestors are concerned with everything that goes on, and should be remembered constantly. Everything that is done should be done in a way that would be pleasing, for if it is not, they may become angered and send sickness and death to the living.

Throughout their daily lives, then, the traditional Africans are constantly remembering the past, remembering their ancestors. They are constantly performing little ritual acts. They do not always make a great fuss; it may amount to no more than throwing a few grains of food into the forest. Or it may be a great ceremony in which hundreds of members of the tribe take part, involving weeks of preparation. But all the time, every day, the ancestors are remembered in some way.

There are certain occasions, like birth, when it is particularly important to remember. This is taken pretty much as a matter of course, but there are always some special things that have to be done, offerings to be made to the family shrine, perhaps. And when the child is named, which may not be for some time, it is an even more important occasion, and he may be given the name of some elderly or dead relative, so that a name never dies with the body. The next important occasion during the life of the individual occurs when he or she is ready to take on adult responsibilities. This is the time for initiation of one kind or another. It prepares you further for this life, but it also prepares you for the next, and makes you pleasing to the ancestors. This is often the biggest and most important of all tribal ceremonies.

Then comes marriage, and married life is full of small daily observances as the couple go about their work. For them the final act is, of course, death and burial. Burial may be accomplished with little formality, as among the hunters or Masai pastoralists. Among the cultivators, it is generally attended by much more elaborate ritual, and in the case of the complex tribes with chiefs or kings at their head, the burial of the nobility can be extremely costly, calling for a long period of mourning during which the bereaved family sometimes has to feed all the mourners, making great sacrifices.

On all these occasions the family takes part, the number of relatives included depending on the particular context. There are times, then, when the family unites, when members who are otherwise separated may meet and renew old friendships. Probably death brings more of the family together than any other event, and the death of a chief or king involves the entire family—that is to say the tribe or nation. So once again we see the African sense of family loyalty emerging, here on occasions of what might be called crisis. For in a sense even marriage is a crisis, for it involves either the boy's or girl's leaving his or her parents and joining another group as a stranger; it means that they have committed their families just as they are bound as individuals; it means that each is now to be put to the real test.

At times of lesser crisis the family need not be called upon to take part, but the people may use what we loosely refer to as magic. It is difficult for us to understand because much of the magic that is performed is obviously, to us, without any effect. When a man lets some moss fall from his fingers, held above his head, and blows on it so that it blows away from him, we know that this will not cause the rain clouds to pass over him, as he hopes they will. Maybe he knows it too though, and it may be no more than calling the attention of the ancestors, the spirits, or of God himself, to his plight. Many so-called magical acts are really acts of faith and correspond more to the western notion of prayer than anything else.

Then there are moments when the individual feels powerless and asks for help from the ritual specialist, that much-misunderstood person we generally call the witch doctor. He would be better known simply as the doctor, because he has much the same kind of profession. Often he knows medically effective treatments, some of them even more powerful than modern drugs, such as antidotes to snake bite, and antiseptics used on open wounds. When he does not know a remedy, however, he pretends that he does. We all know that if a sick person believes that he is going to get well, part of the battle is already won. And so it may be that the belief in the doctor, even if his medicines and incantations are of no medical use, will help toward recovery.

But the doctor is more than just the healer of bodies. He is also often the healer of wounded pride, of hostility, of enmity. Because of the importance of his position and the fact that he is so greatly respected, he usually knows everything that is going on in the community. So when someone falls ill, he may give his verdict that the illness has been caused by someone else causing the sick person harm by witchcraft. This is a serious accusation, and everyone will want to know who the witch is.

The belief is that witchcraft is a substance which is usually found in the stomach. The witch may not even know that he has it, and it makes him do things he would not do otherwise. He can not be absolutely blamed for what it makes him do, but if he finds he has it, he has either got to get rid of it in some way, or render it ineffective.

The doctor will find out who the witch is by divination. Throwing bones or using a rubbing board are some of his methods. The bones fall in a certain pattern which he interprets much like reading tea leaves in a cup. The rubbing board is rubbed with a finger or a lump of wood while the doctor asks it questions. When his finger sticks, he has the answer Yes. He will ask all sorts of questions, and because of his knowledge of

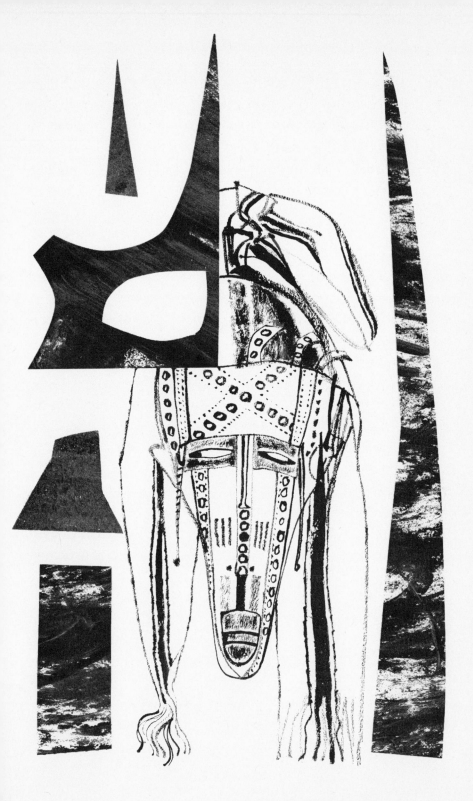

Mask from French Sudan

all the local gossip, and by watching his patient very carefully, he will eventually name someone who perhaps had some personal grievance against the sick man. That person is formally accused of being a witch, and of course he will deny it. All he has to do is to take medicine that will render the witchcraft substance harmless, if he has it, and then everyone is happy. He is not punished in any way, though he may have to pay a small fine of some chickens, and perhaps drink beer with his enemy, or provide a feast to show publicly that there has been a reconciliation.

You may ask how this helps, what good it does. It may not help the sick man get well, although it may give him confidence. It is done primarily because in this way the enmity between the two people is made public—everyone knows about it. This means that they will not dare to harm each other in any way, because then they will be accused immediately, and this time they will, if found guilty, be subject to much more serious punishment. In this way the doctor helps greatly to keep the peace and the law in his community.

Sorcery is something quite different, and is everywhere regarded as evil. It is believed that certain people who have this witchcraft substance in their stomachs come to know about it and deliberately use it to further their own ends. Or else they may sell their power to others. Nobody will ever admit to being a sorcerer, for by definition a sorcerer is an enemy of society, while a doctor is its protector. Even so, the belief that such people exist is not a meaningless fantasy.

Suppose a violent quarrel breaks out between two members of a tribe, and in a fight the one accidentally kills the other. We would say that he was guilty of manslaughter or murder and punish him accordingly. But in Africa the traditional legal system works differently. An African tribunal would investigate the cause of the quarrel, and might find that in fact the man who died was a real troublemaker and had provoked the fight. Someone has to be made responsible for the death, otherwise a feud would result between the two families, each killing each other in retaliation; yet to accuse the survivor of murder would be an obvious injustice.

He can not, however, be excused by saying he was made to kill by witchcraft substance in his stomach, because generally witchcraft substance works at night when the witch is asleep and does not know about it. This man killed in daylight, in the middle of a fight. So then the doctor says that the cause was sorcery. As nobody ever admits to being a sorcerer, there is nobody to punish; but the man actually responsible for the death is excused. The doctor "proves" his case by divination, or by consulting some oracle and getting the appropriate answer. He will give his judgment, not saying that the dead man deserved to die, but that some sorcerer, unknown, caused his death through the hand of the man who fought him. He will say that the power of the sorcerer is great, and that it must be defeated by an even more powerful sacrifice.

In this way he threatens everyone concerned, hinting that if they do not do what he says, then more killings will occur. He tells them to kill a goat and prepare a feast for the ancestors. He supervises the ritual side of the feast, but an essential part is that the two families—that of the dead man and that of his slayer—are made to sit down together and share the same food. This is a sign that peace is restored between them, that there will be no feud. The honor of the dead man's family is maintained; the man responsible for the death is not held responsible, but will probably have to pay the cost of the feast in order to "clean the blood from his hands."

To the African the letter of the law is not so important as the spirit of the law. The spirit of the law involves a sense of family obligation, either at the level of the individual family or that of the tribe. The doctor, or witch doctor, is one of the people best fitted to interpret the law in this spirit, and the beliefs in magic, witchcraft, and sorcery enable him to do so with extreme justice and wisdom. Without these institutions he would be powerless, and there would be no law.

There are other things which sound even stranger to our ears, and which might appear even more "savage." Yet again if we look at them in their whole context, they seem quite different, and understandable. Let's take just one, perhaps the most frightening of all—the Leopard Man Society. There are various forms of this spread widely across West and central Africa, differing greatly from each other. Perhaps the best known, and the most misunderstood, is the *anyota* society of the BaBali people, in the east-central Congo. The common idea about the society was that its members simply dressed up as leopards and went off, usually at the command of the chief, to kill his enemies. They were thought of as common murderers and cannibals. But in fact they were something quite different and were highly respected.

In times of crisis, the great need in tribal life is for the tribe to be firmly united. If the tribe weakens and divides amongst itself, then neighboring tribes may combine and attack. One of the most dangerous times of all, as we saw when we looked at the kingdoms, occurs when a chief or king dies. Amongst the BaBali people the chief may have several wives, and the sons of any of them may succeed him. There is a great deal of rivalry between the wives, each one naturally wanting her son to become the new chief. Because of family feeling, the tribe will divide its loyalties, each group supporting its own family member. Something has to be done to bring the people together, rapidly and effectively. The *anyota* society exists for this purpose.

Its members are chosen when they have proven themselves, as youths, to be strong and fit, and above all to be respectful of the ways of the ancestors. They are bound by the most powerful oaths. At times of crisis, when the problem is acute and can not readily be solved in any other way, the members of the *anyota* take action. They dress like leopards, painting the body with spots, covering it with a leopard skin or spotted cloth, wearing a leopard mask. As they do this they gradually identify themselves with this, their chosen symbol, the leopard. They fix metal claws to their hands, razor sharp, and they *become* leopards.

The leopard is the symbol of death, for it brings death silently, swiftly, and without discrimination. The leopard strikes young and old, good and bad; its behavior can never be predicted. It is as sure as it is mysterious, and it also possesses many of the qualities admired by the Africans. It has the beauty and grace of a dancer, the physical strength and courage of a hunter and fighter. But above all it is the bringer of death. The ancestors have passed beyond death, and it is impossible to join them without dying. They may be invoked to give aid, but the way of the *anyota* is more direct.

A man becomes a leopard. He loses all his personal identity; he moves and thinks like the bringer of death. He stands at the threshold of death and of the afterlife. Through this identification he is able to contact the ancestors in the world beyond death, and receive their instructions. Acting on their instructions, with their blessing, he lives for a short while as a leopard; he lies in wait, and he kills. He does *not* choose his victim because he belongs to this family or that, because now he thinks like a leopard, not a man. So he hides in a tree, down by the river, just where the leopards would, and he chooses his victims just as a leopard would. This means that he generally kills women and children, for a leopard will not attack a group of armed men, or any large group of people. But he will kill a single woman or child coming down to get water. And having killed, just like the leopard, tearing the jugular vein with his claws, the leopard-man eats—just like the leopard. A small portion of the body is eaten; the rest is left. After this he becomes a man again, and he does not know what he has done.

The villagers find the body, and they know what has happened, for although one such killing may be thought to be a real leopard, a whole series will not. And although the *anyota* leave leopard footprints with a special wooden club they use, they can not always hide their human tracks. Usually after a couple of killings the people know for certain that the *anyota* is taking action. They know that for as long as the crisis continues, for as long as they continue to disagree amongst themselves, the ancestors will command the *anyota* to kill and eat. The killing is horrible enough, particularly as no one knows who is going to be killed next. But even worse for these people is the thought that their own people are eating human flesh, for this is as repugnant to them as it is to us. It is precisely because the whole thing is so terrible that the society does its job. The disagreement is quickly resolved, and once the tribe is united again, the ancestors are pacified, and the *anyota* is forgotten. But the threat is always there, and it serves as a constant warning.

In a way, the tribe has committed a crime against the ancestors by disagreeing amongst itself. It is a crime that could bring disaster, even death, to innocent members particularly if they are invaded by a hostile tribe. So there has to be punishment, and the situation has to be resolved. This is their way of doing it. Everyone shares the responsibility equally, the tribe being considered at this level as one family, so the punishment may fall anywhere with equal justice. And with only one or two deaths, perhaps the whole tribe is saved. Viewed in this light, as a means of preserving the tribe from even greater evil, it is better understood.

And so it is with so many of the customs we consider as strange and barbaric. We have to try and see them in their proper surroundings, not to imagine them as being part of our own society. And if we do this, we find that even when customs seem most different from our own, they are usually working for exactly the same ends that we consider right and good: the maintenance of accepted morality, the preservation of individual rights, the safety of the tribe (or nation), in accordance with their belief in the will of the ancestors or God.

NEW FOR OLD

There are still in Africa today many millions of people who continue to live largely according to the tribal tradition. We have seen something of how widely different these traditions can be, and of how each one can only really be understood in its own context. Each in its own way is satisfactory, because it gives the people what they want. It gives them food, clothing, and shelter, and it gives them security—both security in this world and in the next, according to their beliefs.

But the tradition is such that even though it is not fixed and static, it can only grow from the inside. Contact with the western world has been far too rapid for tradition to be able to adapt itself effectively. For instance, in many areas colonial powers have forbidden certain initiation rites, marriage practices, or ceremonial festivals. And everywhere the economy has been changed, as has the political power of the chief. The result is that tradition either fights back, becoming ultraconservative, or else it simply collapses. Either way it is doomed, because by being ultraconservative it loses its flexibility, and this is what has made it the power it is. Yet the moment it accepts forced change in one of its many interlocking customs, the whole system collapses.

Had there been time, tradition could have adapted itself, even to far-reaching changes such as these. At the moment there is real danger that all tradition will be lost. Luckily we have been able to record much that has already gone from everyday practice, and Africans themselves are becoming more and more interested in their tribal past. But there are still very real difficulties that stand in the way of reconciling the two worlds, the old and the new.

The colonial boundaries, and even those of the new independent nations, join together many tribes that have no common values at all. For instance, in Kenya there are still small bands of hunters like the Ndorobo, with their beliefs; pastoralists like the Masai, who feel that they are superior to all other men because their god gave them cattle; and cultivators like the Kikuyu, traditional enemies of the Masai, believing in land rather than cattle. The belief of the Masai in their tradition is so strong that they not only refuse to live any other way than by raising cattle, but they refuse to have any more to do with non-cattle people than is absolutely necessary. They live on a reservation and take little or no part in national politics.

The Kikuyu, much more adaptable, still retain their belief in land, but this does not stop them from taking a leading role in the government of their country. This means that sooner or later the Masai have to face up to the fact that even if they stay on their reservation, for as long as their cattle survive, they will in fact be taking orders from Kikuyu officials. It is difficult to see any traditional Masai accepting such orders.

The Bushmen and Pygmies, like the Masai, are not willing to abandon their way of life, and unless they do, they too are doomed. In a sense they are doomed anyway, for if they do abandon their old ways, they will no longer be the people they are now.

So we have to make up our minds to the fact that the process of change, which is by no means foreign to Africa, is going to continue. But because the ways of people change, that does not mean that all their beliefs have to change. This would be the greatest tragedy that could happen, for the African peoples believe in the family, its obligations and responsibilities. They believe in a respect for life, and they tolerate other forms of life even though they may consider their own the best. They believe that their world is a good place, and that this goodness grows

out of respect for the ancestors and out of the existence of some unseen, often unknown, all-powerful being that has the welfare of the living to heart.

What has to be done is to guide the process of the change so that there are no gaps left in the lives of the tribal peoples. We saw how magic and witchcraft, although they are scorned as much by the educated Africans as by anyone else, do in fact have an important part to play in tribal society. If you destroy the belief in magic and witchcraft, or if you make it unlawful, then you are creating a gap. How will disputes be settled without causing a rift in the society? How will personal grievances be aired in public so that they never reach dangerous limits? And if initiation is forbidden, or if it is simply made impossible because of compulsory schooling or work or whatever, then how are the people to have any incentive to live this life? For without being initiated they believe that they have no place in the next life.

If this belief is taken away from them, then they are not bound any longer by any moral code. It is not enough to say that they can be given another belief—in Christianity or Islam—because someone can not be forced to change his belief overnight, and during the period of transition there can be complete disaster, complete moral breakdown.

These are only some of the problems. It is not enough for Africans to try, as some have tried, to imitate the ways of the western world, even their thoughts and beliefs. Tradition is too powerful for that; they are still African. And even in trying to do it they divorce themselves not only from the past, but from the present.

And yet, ever since the colonial powers have been in Africa, this is what the colonists have been teaching—that the African should completely abandon his old ways and become like the European. There are many who have tried. They are not understood by their own people nor by the Europeans, and they live in a third world of their own, in between the two.

There are others, however, who have seen that change had to come—great change—and who without denying their heritage have accepted whatever seemed right, rejecting the rest. This can be seen to some extent in the way some of the West African nations have behaved since they won independence. They have not accepted completely the form of government that was left them by the colonial powers, though their former rulers seriously believed these forms of government to be best.

In some cases they have adapted parliamentary procedure to something more familiar to them. The parliament still exists, but the way in which the members sit and take part in its discussions is modeled more after the old traditional system of the kings and chiefs and their councils. The value of this is that while it still makes it possible for the one government to govern the whole territory, not just one tribe, in general it has much more the appearance of a tribal court, and so is more familiar to the tribal peoples who live inland and who are not familiar with the western way. In a sense the president becomes a paramount chief, and all the members of parliament become his subchiefs, sitting together equally in council, representing their people.

In ways such as this the tradition of the past may not only be kept alive, but it may make a real contribution to the present. It is impossible to even guess at which of the old customs will survive, but we have seen many of them in their tribal context, and they have much to contribute. If they are properly understood and properly used, their contribution may be of immense value. It will not only give the peoples of Africa a sense of continuity with the past, but it will unite them all the more strongly with each other. There is already a wider recognition of the importance of the heritage that is Africa's, and where this recognition is being acted upon, there is no longer a mere, blind preservation of the old; nor an equally blind adoption of the new; but a vital blending of the two, something new, something African.

CHRONOLOGICAL CHART
OF AFRICA
AND WORLD EVENTS

CHRONOLOGICAL CHART OF

	AFRICA	MEDITERRANEAN WORLD
B.C. **4000–3000**	Remains of man-type in East Africa possibly dating back a million or more years Migrations to Africa from Middle East via Sinai Peninsula Beginning of ancient Egyptian civilization in Nile Valley, about 3200	
3000–2000		Early Minoan Age in Crete, about 3000–2200
2000–1000	Middle Kingdom, 2100–1700: Egypt and Ethiopia centers of contact between Africa and outside world Egyptian invasions of Nubia in northeast Africa, and Syria	
		Minoans leading traders of Mediterranean, about 1800
	New Kingdom, 1555–712: Egyptian empire extends through Palestine and Syria to upper Euphrates	
		Mycenaeans trade with Egypt and Phoenicia, about 1400
		Phoenician city-states flourish; leading traders of Mediterranean, about 1250
	Exodus of Jews from Egypt to Palestine, about 1200	
1000–500	Greeks found colonies in North Africa, about 950 Phoenicians found Carthage in North Africa, 814 Egypt occupied by Nubians, about 712 Assyrians overthrow Nubians; sack Memphis and Thebes, 662	
		Persian Empire founded, 546; extends to Mediterranean
500–1	Persians under Cambysus conquer Egypt, 525 Hanno of Carthage explores west coast of Africa, about 5th century Alexander the Great conquers Egypt and founds capital at Alexandria, 332	
	Punic Wars between Rome and Carthage: Carthage falls to Rome, 146 B.C.	
	North Africa from coast to coast under Roman domination	
A.D. **1–500**		
		Roman Empire master of Mediterranean, 116
	Roman and Greek influences reach down both coasts almost to equator; Far Eastern influences on east coast; early Arab trading posts down east coast	
500–600		
600–700	Arabs conquer Egypt, 646	
		Arabs supreme in eastern Mediterranean

AFRICA AND WORLD EVENTS

	EUROPE	NEAR EAST AND ASIA	WESTERN HEMISPHERE
B.C. 4000–3000		Beginning of Mesopotamian civilization in Tigris-Euphrates Valley at Sumer, about 4500–3000: First farmers arrive at Indus Valley in India, about 4000	
3000–2000	Early Minoan Age in Crete, about 3000–2200	Beginning of Chinese civilization in Yellow River Valley, about 2700	
2000–1000		Beginning of Indian civilization in Indus Valley, 2100–1300 Hammurabi rules from Babylon, about 1800–1780; occupied by Kassites, about 1600	First farmers arrive at Guatemala, Chiapas, and Yucatán, about 2000
	Minoans leading traders of Mediterranean, about 1800; Minoan civilization at height, about 1600		
		Rice cultivation develops in tropical Asia, about 1500	
	Mycenaeans on Greek peninsula replace Minoans; trade with Egypt and Phoenicia, about 1400	Golden Age of Hittite civilization, about 1400	
		Aryans invade India, about 1200	
	Trojan War, 1190–1184		Peruvian Indian cultures begin, about 1200
1000–500	Greek city-states, about 950 Rome founded, 753	Assyrian power at height, 750 Buddha in India, about 560–487: Confucius in China, 551–479	
	Persian Empire founded, 546; extends from Mediterranean to India under Darius	Babylon falls, 539	
500–1	Golden Age of Greek civilization Alexander the Great, 336–323, spreads Greek civilization over known Western world to India	Great Wall of China built, 246–210: Unification of Chinese Empire	
	Trade routes between Far East and West: Roman trade reaches India, about 50 B.C.		
A.D. 1–500	Roman Empire founded, 27 B.C. Christian Church founded, about 42 A.D. Roman empire at greatest extent, 116		
		Eastern Roman Empire founded at Constantinople, 330	Maya period of prosperity, 300–700
	Final division into Eastern Roman Empire (Byzantium) and Western European Empire (Rome), 395 Sack of Rome by Goths, 410		
500–600	Beginning of modern Western European civilization	Great advancement of Byzantine civilization, 527–565	
600–700		Beginning of Moslem Era, 622, and Arab Empire, 632; Arabs conquer Persia and Egypt	

CHRONOLOGICAL CHART OF

	AFRICA	MEDITERRANEAN WORLD

700–800	North Africa conquered by Arabs, 709
	    Conversion to Islam
	    Trading settlements move inland; traffic in slaves and ivory	

800–900	Moors from North Africa sweep northward into Spain	
900–1000		
1000–1100		
1100–1200		Crusades against Moslems in Holy Lands, 1096–1270
1200–1300	Western Sudan converted to Islam Nation of Ghana on west coast of Africa	
1300–1400		
1400–1500	Henry the Navigator, 1394–1460, directs Portuguese voyages along African coast	
	Bartholomeu Dias rounds Cape of Good Hope, 1488, opening trade route to East: Mediterranean trade routes replaced	
1500–1600		
1600–1700	Establishment on W, S, and E coasts of Africa of posts to supply food and water to European trading ships bound to and from India	
1700–1800	Arab slave traders sell slaves from east coast to Orient; sell slaves from west coast to British, French, Portuguese, and Spanish settlements in Americas	
1800–1900	"Scramble for Africa" by European powers seeking economic resources for development Colonization by British, French, Belgians, Italians, Germans	Mediterranean resumes importance as trade link after Suez Canal, 1869
1900–	African countries win independence from colonial powers, 1956— Ghana; Sierra Leone; Gambia; Senegal; Mauretania; Mali; Guinea; Upper Volta; Ivory Coast; Togo; Dahomey; Niger; Chad; Central African Republic; Cameroun; Gabon; Congo-Brazzaville; Congo-Leopoldville; Rwanda; Burundi; Tanganyika; Kenya; Uganda; Sudan; Somalia; Malagasy Republic; Nigeria	

AFRICA AND WORLD EVENTS

	EUROPE	NEAR EAST AND ASIA	WESTERN HEMISPHERE
700–800	Arabs conquer Spain, 713 Arab expansion into Europe stopped by defeat at Tours, 732	Golden Age of Arab Empire, 750–1258	
800–900	Charlemagne crowned emperor of Holy Roman Empire at Rome, 800; Christianity introduced to many European nations, 800–990	Byzantine civilization flourishes, 867–1056	
900–1000	Arab rule in Spain at height: Cordova greatest intellectual center in Europe		Eric the Red discovers Greenland, about 985
1000–1100	William the Conqueror invades England, 1066	Seljuk Turks seize Baghdad, 1055; defeat Byzantines in Armenia, 1071	Leif Ericson visits Vinland, about 1000
	Crusades against Moslems in Holy Lands, 1096–1270		
1100–1200			
1200–1300	Magna Charta in England, 1215 Golden Horde (Tatars) in Russia, 1240–1480	Genghis Khan conquers Central Asia and China, 1206–1221 Mongols destroy Baghdad; overthrow Arab Empire, 1258 Ottoman Turks found empire, 1288	
1300–1400	Ottoman Turks defeat Serbs, absorb Bulgars, 1389; Byzantine Empire suffers greatly		
1400–1500	Renaissance Invention of printing by movable type, 1439	Tamerlane, 1369–1405, rules from Turkey to China, including parts of India Ottoman Turks control most of Asia; block trade routes to Far East: End of Byzantine Empire, 1453; control Arabs, 1453–1923	Rise of Aztec civilization
	Moors expelled from Spain: Beginning of Spanish exploration in New World		Columbus discovers America, 1492
	Vasco da Gama reaches India, 1498		Aztec and Inca civilizations at height
1500–1600	Magellan voyages around the world, 1519–1522 Beginning of European commercial interest in India		Cortés in Mexico, 1519–1521; Pizarro in Peru, 1531–1535
1600–1700	First charter of British East India Co., 1600–1858		Pilgrims land at Plymouth, 1620
1700–1800	Beginning of Industrial Revolution French Revolution, 1788–1799		American Revolution, 1775–1783 Declaration of Independence, 1776
1800–1900	Napoleon defeated at Waterloo, 1815		Civil War in U. S., 1861–1865 Abolition of slavery
	Suez Canal, 1869, opens shorter trade route to E Asia: European empires established throughout Asia and Africa		
1900–	W. W. I., 1914–1918	Chinese Revolution, 1911–1912 End of Turkish Empire in Near East, 1923: Creation of independent Arab states	U. S. enters W. W. I., 1917
	World War II, 1939–1945		U. S. enters W. W. II., 1941
	U. N. created, 1942; establish headquarters in U. S., 1946		
		Partition of India into Pakistan and Republic of India, 1947	

BOOKS FOR FURTHER READING

Bovill, E. W., *The Golden Trade of the Moors*. New York, Oxford University Press, 1958.

Buckley, Peter, *Okolo of Nigeria*. New York, Simon and Schuster, Inc., 1962.

Davidson, Basil, *The Lost Cities of Africa*. Boston, Little, Brown and Co. (Atlantic Monthly Press), 1959.

Dinesen, Isak, *Out of Africa*. New York, Modern Library, 1952.

Gluckman, Max, *Custom and Conflict in Africa*. New York, Free Press of Glencoe, 1956.

Gunther, John, *Meet the Congo and Its Neighbors*. New York, Harper & Brothers, 1959.

————, and others, *Meet South Africa*. New York, Harper & Brothers, 1958.

Mead, Margaret, *People and Places,* pp. 153–169 (Ashanti). Cleveland and New York, The World Publishing Company, 1959.

Paton, Alan, *Land and People of South Africa*. Philadelphia, J. B. Lippincott Co., 1955.

Thomas, Elizabeth Marshall, *The Harmless People*. New York, Alfred A. Knopf, Inc., 1959.

Turnbull, Colin M., *The Forest People*. New York, Simon and Schuster, Inc., 1961.

————, *The Lonely African*. New York, Simon and Schuster, Inc., 1962.

van der Post, Laurens, *The Heart of the Hunter*. New York, William Morrow and Co., Inc., 1961.

————, *Venture to the Interior*. New York, William Morrow and Co., Inc., 1951.

INDEX AND GLOSSARY

ABOUT THE AUTHOR

COLIN TURNBULL, an author and anthropologist who has
met and lived with the African people during three extensive
tours of the continent, had what he calls an "accidental introduction" to Africa. "I did not have enough money to
return to England from India, so I took a deck passage to
Mombasa, got a motorcycle in Nairobi and went through
Africa on that, stopping overnight in villages and eating
whatever the local food was. This was the best possible way
of really meeting the African people." Since that first visit in
1951 he has traveled by station wagon across the Sahara
Desert and from the west coast to the east coast of Africa.

Dr. Turnbull was born in England and studied anthro-
pology and philosophy at Oxford University, the School of
Oriental and African Studies at London University, and
Banaras Hindu University in India. Author of two books,
The Forest People and *The Lonely African,* he is at present
Assistant Curator, in charge of African Ethnology at the
American Museum of Natural History in New York City.

7 8 9 10 71 70 69 68